A Glimpse of Eternity

Alejandro Tuama

The author kindly acknowledges the following books from which he has used a
limited number of quotes. All copyright remains with the original. In event of
any queries, please contact the publisher in the first instance:
p. 102: *The Murder of Christ* by Wilhelm Reich (1953)
pp. 107–108: *Jitterbug Perfume* by Tom Robbins (1984)
p. 233: *The Unbearable Lightness of Being* by Milan Kundera (1984)

Cover Design by Daniel Hill | danjisdesigns.com

Part One
The Sacred Valley
June 2016

Chapter One
The Sanctuary

What I notice first in Cusco are all the dogs. This is a city for strays, it seems. They move in packs or sleep alone on the pavement or on the street. A shaggy spaniel with a matted brown coat gnaws at its paws in the middle of the road, and my taxi-driver, Dennis, has to honk his horn to get the little mongrel to move.

A raspy cough rattles my chest and my stomach gurgles from plane food and angst. This all just seems so surreal. I'm not excited. No, this is some kind of sham excitement. It feels as though a previous Nicholas – a Nicholas of six months ago, from the comfort of his friend's living room in Perth – booked this trip to South America, and now the current Nicholas, *me*, actually has to go through with it.

I'm too exhausted to attempt a conversation with Dennis, so I lean my forehead against the cold glass of the passenger's window. We pass dusty workshops and fruit stalls, produce spread out on colourful patterned blankets or piled into wicker baskets. Outdoor mechanics work with cigarettes hanging from

1

their lips, and young women walk the streets in blue jeans, with their shiny black hair tied in long ponytails. There are construction sites, it seems, on each street we pass. Every few blocks holds a work-in-progress, puffing out fumes and dust and sand. The city seems unfinished.

When we arrive at The Sanctuary, a boutique bed and breakfast on the outskirts of Cusco, a woman is waiting, perched in the shade and leaning against the outer wall of her property. She's wearing denim jeans and a t-shirt, and her hair is cut short. Her skin is the colour of well-worn leather and her face is dotted with freckles. She's about the same age as my mother, so late 50s, early 60s.

'Welcome to my house, Nicholas,' she says as I approach. 'I am Eliza.'

'Nice to meet you Eliza, ahh *mucho gusto.*'

Eliza smiles, pays the driver, then leads me through the black electronic gate. Behind the gate a flat stone path flanked by fruit trees, rose bushes and shrubs leads up a slight incline towards the house. To the right of the path sits a small coffee table and chairs. To the left, amongst the trees and shrubs, are two bird baths and a small plaster statue of a child holding a vase. Ahead, the house stretches out wide and long, with tanned wooden doors, whitewashed walls and a terracotta tiled roof. Beyond the house rises a green mountain dotted with pine trees. A landslide, it seems, has carved a great scar across the mountain's face.

Eliza shows me inside and through to my room. Outside my door is a small table with a kettle, teapot and a selection of teas.

'Coca tea,' says Eliza, pointing to a green packet. 'Good for the altitude.'

I smile and nod. 'I feel a little dizzy.'

'Tell me if you have headache, oh-kay?' Her eyes are soft, and she looks at me like I remind her of another time in her life.

'I will. Thank you, Eliza.'

'I can make you a salad for your lunch today. Is this enough for you?'

'Yes, that's great. I don't eat meat.' It's easier to just say I don't eat meat rather than trying to explain the strict diet I'm supposed to follow.

'Please come to the dining room when you are ready.'

I lay my bags down on the floorboards and collapse onto my bed.

The dining room is decorated with polished dark wooden furniture, soft lounges draped in frilled upholstery, and paintings of horses, churches and country landscapes. I run my fingers and eyes across the bookshelf while Eliza clatters away in the kitchen next door. The house is clearly vacuumed and dusted regularly, yet still there's the faint perfume of an old people's home. Eliza calls out from the kitchen, and I take a seat at the dining table.

'Here you are, my darling,' she says, as she lays out a plate of sliced cucumber, tomato, lettuce leaves, salted avocado, shredded carrot, beetroot and lime wedges.

'*Muchos gracias.*'

Eliza excuses herself so I sit alone at the table – large enough to host an extravagant dinner party – flicking through guidebooks, seeking information on Iquitos, the gateway to the Peruvian Amazon.

After lunch I sort through and rearrange my bags. Items of note are the five pairs of premium breathable boxer briefs, a quick-dry travel towel, my black *10,000 Days* t-shirt and my light blue Terence McKenna t-shirt. Jammed into my daypack is my writing journal, a soft-cover copy of my favourite novel, *Jitterbug Perfume,* plus *Slaughterhouse-Five*, *Prometheus Rising* and a pocket-size Spanish phrase book. In the top pouch of my daypack is a pendant of Saint Cristopher from my father and a black tourmaline stone from my mother.

Having sorted out my gear, I shift the furniture around in my room so the writing desk faces into the garden courtyard rather than against a wall. I scribble a few pages in my journal but I'm halted by the knot of anxiety tightening around my belly.

It's probably just jetlag and altitude.

Eliza knocks on my door to offer more coca tea. 'I am making lentils for dinner tonight,' she says. 'For myself and for the cleaning staff as well. I'm sorry that we don't have something more substantial to offer, but would you like me to make for you as well?'

'Yes please. Lentils are perfect.'

A chainsaw fires off in the distance, and Eliza looks out the window into her garden. Her face sinks. 'Will you go into the city, Nicholas?'

'Tomorrow after breakfast, depending on how I'm feeling.' I softly blow on my cup of coca tea.

'There is a lot more construction around Cusco these days. In the city especially, but also out here. More tourism brings more money and more construction.'

I break Eliza's gaze and look down sheepishly at my tea.

'It is almost impossible to stop this development.'

'What do you mean, *development?*'

'I mean, Nicholas, that my house used to be surrounded by trees, by the forest.'

'This used to be the countryside?'

'That's right. Now we are surrounded by buildings. The city has stretched out to engulf us.'

'That's a shame,' I say.

It doesn't matter where in the world you are. You can't escape the human. It's what we do. We spread. Like a virus.

At dinner that evening Eliza asks why I came to Cusco. I pause to think for a moment and take a mouthful of lentils. Eliza looks on wistfully.

'I've been interested in South and Central America for a long time,' I say. 'My mother studied Ancient History and Art when I was a kid. I used to love flicking through her assignments on the Incas and the Mayans and the Aztecs. Something about the temples and the pantheons, it just seemed so otherworldly, and exciting, and well… *magical.* At least it did when I was a child.'

I remember gravitating to my parent's office as a young boy, in the house we lived in when they were still together. There was a wooden leather-top writing desk that smelled oily and rich and was so large that I could barely see past the far edge. Around the room were wall-to-wall bookshelves, with two complete sets of encyclopaedias and ten years' worth of National Geographic magazines, bursting with glossy colour photos. Propped up on pillows, I'd sit at the office chair enclosed in piles of books and magazines. I'd pour over the photos and illustrations in my mother's textbooks and the colour-photocopy pictures in her university assignments until I overflowed with wonder and excitement and yearning.

Eliza smiles. 'What do you do for work, Nicholas?'

'I'm a high school teacher.'

'You teach history? You will go to Machu Picchu?'

'Ah, no. I teach English. And Psychology.'

Eliza raises an eyebrow.

'But yes, I will go to Machu Pichu. Two friends will join me in about two weeks. We're going to hike the Inca Trail.'

'And what are your plans before your friends arrive?'

'I'm going to Urubamba this weekend.'

'Beautiful. And what will you do in the Sacred Valley?'

I hesitate. 'Ahh, I'm going to be doing some *ceremonies*.'

'Yes,' she gently nods, 'Ayahuasca.'

Was it that obvious?

'I could see it in your eyes,' she says. 'Be careful, Nicholas. Ayahuasca is a sacred medicine. It must be approached with respect.'

'Are you experienced?'

'I have drunk the medicine. And both of my children have drunk the medicine also. My son is an apprentice ayahuascero. He is training in the jungle.'

Eliza shares some of her experiences with ayahuasca. She tells me of the time when she could speak telepathically with her friend. And the time when an ayahuascero recounted *her* visions from the night so precisely, it was as though he were actually *in* her mind. Now she gazes pensively out the window into her garden.

I booked an ayahuasca retreat in Urubamba for this coming weekend on my mate Harry's specific recommendation. He's the only guy I know, besides Eliza, who's ever actually taken ayahuasca. Just about every time I saw him, Harry would find a way to steer the conversation onto how ayahuasca changed his life.

I met Harry through my best mate Stan. Harry was, and still is I guess, Stan's primary weed dealer. Harry's an interesting guy. He lives out in the Perth hills with his young family, two dogs, three chickens and fifteen dope plants. He's the kind of

6

guy that's always got a new conspiracy theory to discuss. I wouldn't text him to hang out, but if we were at the same party, I'd have a beer with him. I just wouldn't want to get stuck talking with him for too long.

Anyway, Harry told me that when he drank ayahuasca he spoke with aliens and angels and jungle spirits and a giant snake and fucken fractal frangipanis or something like that. He faced his inner demons – whatever that actually means – and came out the other side reborn. I felt obliged at least to book in for a weekend at the place where he stayed. I didn't know how much of what Harry said in his long rants was real and how much was bullshit, but he was very compelling. I figured if even half of what he said was true, then it was worth looking into.

As well as this little place that Harry recommended in Urubamba, I've been in communication with someone from another retreat centre. It's called Way of the Spirit Healing Centre, and it's located in Iquitos, in the Peruvian Amazon. I'll be heading there with my friends after the Inca Trail, if all goes to plan.

I ask Eliza if I'm the only person staying at the hotel, and she says that a couple of families from other regions of Peru will be staying but not until after I've left. I thank her for breakfast then retire to my room, where it smells of mango, cabbage and isolation.

Lying on my bed, I can clearly recall the last conversation I had with my father before I left for this trip. We were at the pub, and I was trying my best to explain why I was heading to South America to drink the world's most powerful psychedelic plants.

'To be honest, Dad, I'm lost,' I said to him. 'I don't know what I'm doing with my life and I'm scared I'll look back in ten years with regret.' I usually avoid laying on too much of a trip with my parents, but after a couple of beers, I found the words falling out of my mouth.

'I get that Nicko,' he said, smiling but unable to hide his concern. 'But you know there's nothing wrong with living a normal life, mate.'

'It's a normal life that I'm most afraid of, and this plant is supposed to be able to help you figure out what to do. The other thing is, Dad, apparently it helps with depression.'

My father smiled. We'd recently started to talk to each other about our emotions.

'I've stopped taking the antidepressants,' I said. 'Are you still on them?'

He nodded. 'I need them, mate. Besides, along with a bottle of wine at night they help me get to a nice plateau. And that's good enough for me.'

'Apparently, these plants help you to get to the core of the depression. You confront your "inner demons",' I said, making the quote signs with my fingers. 'And then you don't need to take the meds anymore.'

'I've told you before that these psycho-whatsit-drugs scare the shit outta me,' he said. Despite his unease, his face showed understanding, or perhaps it was resignation. He took a sip from his glass of red, sighed and softened. 'You're a smart young man, and you always seem to know what you're doing. But Jesus, Nicko, be careful what you wish for.'

And the old man may well prove to be right. I really don't know what I've got myself into over here. I'd be lying if I said I wasn't nervous for this weekend. All I have to base my expectations for ayahuasca on are Harry's rants.

Well, those and the two times I smoked dimethyltryptamine.

The first time I took DMT was in March of this year at Harry's place out in Roleystone in the eastern hills of Perth. We were down by the creek at the edge of his property, surrounded by trees and birds and kangaroos. Just seconds after inhaling, the trees and shrubs around me morphed from grey and green to pulsating purple and yellow and blue, and their branches boogied wildly like seaweed in an ocean storm. I don't remember much of the experience, except for a magical plant entity with exploding columns of light bursting out from its core. Just when I thought I was going to be sucked into a gigantic flower, the drug pulled back, and the vibrancy around me softened. The plants returned to their normal state, but the world seemed crisper, and a little cartoonish. The peak had come and gone, and despite the intensity of the trip, I knew that I hadn't taken enough for what Harry calls a 'breakthrough'.

Three weeks later I was teaching a Year 12 psychology class and halfway through the lesson was halted by a powerful intuitive message that I'd be smoking DMT again soon. I briefly stopped what I was writing on the whiteboard, detached from my body, and observed myself teaching. *I'm standing at the front of a classroom with a whiteboard marker in my hand. Twenty-seven pairs of eyes are looking at me as I deliver a class on memory.* 'Content, content, blah blah blah,' I heard myself say, and the students wrote in their notebooks. 'Something something, the fallibility of memory...'

Out-of-body experiences happen sometimes in teaching. This is meta-teaching. Thinking about teaching, while teaching. The mind observing itself in action.

When the bell rang the students rushed out, and I observed myself reminding them of the homework like I was in some cheesy high school coming-of-age film. That's who I'd become: the teacher in someone else's coming-of-age story.

Later that night, true to my ominous intuition, I smoked DMT for the second time. I was in Maylands, sitting on my own out the back of my best mate Stan's house having a beer amongst the busted fairy lights lying neglected in the sand, just staring at defiant weeds bursting through the cracks in the pavement.

I'd been staying with Stan for about six months. Stan's been my closest mate since we met in high school. We played footy together. Drank beers together. Took drugs together. And most importantly, listened to music together. Every important concert I've been to, Stan's been by my side. He even came along with me and my old man to see Budgie play at the Charles Hotel. So, when I asked him if I could crash at his place for a while, he welcomed me with open arms.

I did of course wonder if twenty-seven was too old to be living in the spare room of your mate's house. Most of my friends have their own places already. Some even have investment properties. I guess I've just got different priorities. To me, a house is a set of chains. I feel no compulsion to get into debt for something that would only serve to tie me down further into a life I don't want. I'd be fastening my own shackles. No thanks. That's why I took a temporary teaching contract at a suburban high school, rented a cheap room at Stan's place, and saved all my money for a plane ticket to get me the fuck out of there.

Anyway, Stan was at his girlfriend's house, so I had the place to myself. I finished my beer and tossed it into the bin by the barbecue. The glass clattered as it settled against the other bottles. I rose from my busted old office chair and walked through the backdoor to get another beer. Inside, the house was dimly lit. Most of the lightbulbs were dead because we're too goddamned lazy to replace them. Strange shadows hung across the mandarin-cream walls and the framed posters of Conan the Barbarian and Dark Side of the Moon. I opened the fridge and reached for a beer, but my eyes locked onto the little Tupperware box full of DMT I'd accepted from Harry the morning after my first experience out at his place in Roleystone. I took the Tupperware box out of the fridge and left it on the kitchen table.

Lying down on the kitchen floor, I took some deep breaths, trying to come to grips with what I'd just decided to do.

After showering in the spare bathroom, I changed into some loose-fitting clothes, then dragged a small white coffee table from the living-room outside, so I could rest Stan's bong onto it and avoid spillages once the drug rendered me incapacitated. In the kitchen I loaded up the cone-piece with a pinch of Stan's weed, then tapped in a knife's tip of DMT and sandwiched the crystals with another sprinkle of weed.

The blood pumped in my belly.

Strong exhale.

There was still time to pull out.

I walked outside into the darkness clutching the bong and sat down at my little coffee table. I placed the bong down securely and took three deep breaths.

Am I really gonna do this?

I lit the dope – careful not to burn the DMT below, just to gently vaporise it – sucked in softly, and held the smoke in my lungs. The taste was burning plastic, metallic and harsh, and it took immediate effect. My skin began to crawl and something strange tugged at the back of my neck. I held as long as I could, then exhaled a cloud of smoke, heart rate intensifying.

I lit the dope again, inhaled softly and held.

Oh, Jesus.

Exhale…

It was *so* fast. And it was *so* strong. *So* much stronger than I'd expected. All sound disappeared except for the deep metronomic pounding of blood in my ear drums. The little white table supporting the bong became golden and bejewelled and started spinning. My head was thick and heavy, and it too was spinning. And holy fuck, the backyard swirled into vibrant technicolour. The plants became seaweed monsters excreting columns of magnificent light. The walls melted down and behind them was the raw flesh of the world, exposed and bleeding and pulsing.

I think I might've had too much. Shit, can you die from this?

The disembodied voice of Terence McKenna reverberated urgently. *Take the third hit, Nicholas*, he cried.

How, Terence?

Just take the Third Hit!

Somehow, I located my hand in space-time and levelled it over the cone-piece for a third time.

Oh Christ! What's happening now? I thought, as the bong itself became golden and bejewelled.

Grab the fucking Royal Goblet, son!

Hands shaking, I lit up the drug and softly inhaled. I took in as much smoke as I could, then took in a little more and held, held, held, and held on a little more, and finally exhaled and...

Oh

My

Fucking Christ Almighty! …*Blast-off* into another world! An alien space of pulsing colour and light, mesmerising and horrifying, enveloped me, surrounded me, infiltrated me. *This is too much to handle!* I thought. But when a strange somersaulting sound split the silence, it was all I could do to just breathe and hold on. It was a *Language*, this sound. They were speaking to me!

Thhhraahhhh! they squealed. *Nnnn. Thromping. Thandros. Thranng!*

Thrrralllll!

The DMT Realm and its mesmerising musical language consumed me and for an age I forgot what I was. It was both horrible and comforting. It was enthralling and yet I desperately wanted it to stop. It was too powerful! This was death by astonishment. I've never been so fucking astonished!

Oh, the Horror! The Horror!

The DMT Realm collapsed, and I was in the backyard once more. Not sure whether to laugh or curl into a ball and sob, I just sat back in the chair and let my mouth hang open. The walls were still pulsing, but the raw flesh of the world was safely concealed behind them. My skin was a sparkling cartoon. I'd never been so relieved to be alive.

In a veiled corner by the barbecue, a shadow-entity said, 'It was a pleasure to meet you, Nicholas. We'll be seeing you again soon.'

Chapter Two
The Push

I manoeuvre one of the thick blankets from my bed at The Sanctuary into a kind of mat so I can stretch on the floor without hurting my legs. Stained light bleeds through the dark red blinds, giving my room a warm and sacred, if not a little ominous, feel. After stretching for about forty-five minutes, I take out my tablet to begin work on the first chapter of my second novel. Just as my fingers touch the keyboard, a car alarm starts blaring, setting off a pack of dogs. A rooster begins to crow, and the workers at a construction site down the road start up a jackhammer.

I sip my tea and press on.

I'm starting my *second* novel now because I've abandoned work on my first: a piece I began when I was living in Melbourne in a Fitzroy apartment with Jessica, my girlfriend at the time. She and I moved east together in 2012 when we realised that Perth held nothing for us. I wrote in my spare time, when I wasn't studying to be a teacher or working at my friend's lighting factory. In our third year in Melbourne, I landed a job at a school out in the Eastern suburbs. I quickly developed a rapport with one of the women in the English department, and as we grew closer over the school year, she became my teaching mentor. Before long, I was sharing extracts from my first novel with her. It was a piece of speculative fiction about virtual reality, the apocalypse, and a modern-day wizard who travels to distant lands in search of a secret technology that could transform consciousness. I gave my mentor what I *thought* was the finished piece so she could pass it along to a friend of hers, a literary agent in Sydney.

Stars were aligning, or so it seemed…

In the meantime, my relationship with Jessica had fallen apart. When we broke up, she moved to London, and I returned alone to Perth – the most isolated major city in the world – with my tail between my legs. I took a job teaching at a high school in a leafy green suburb for a young principal with a sharp suit and a sharp haircut, and I allowed myself to dream that the agent from Sydney would soon contact me, brimming with excitement and flattery, eager to offer me support and advice. I was confident they'd be telling me that publishers had been contacted, and book deals would soon arrive, along with book launches and fancy cocktail party invites, big-shot film producers seeking exclusive movie rights, adoring female readers seeking exclusive fellatio rights, and all that…

At times, I still allow myself to imagine that novel as my ticket out of the rat race. I know I'm delusional, but sometimes I think if only it were published, then no longer would I have to slave away with the rest of the poor saps. Finally, I'd be recognised for my creative genius. Finally, the fame and fortune I'm entitled to would be delivered.

I haven't heard from my mentor for over a year now. I guess her friend, the agent from Sydney, didn't like my novel. Either that or she doesn't even exist. I'm not sure which reality pill is harder to swallow.

But that's okay. I've let all that go now.

Honestly, I have…

The only thing for me to do is pick myself back up and write another novel. This time it'll be The Great Travel Novel. It'll be the novel I wanted to read when I was in high school. *Misunderstood middle-class white boy travels to foreign lands in search of adventure, mysterious Indigenous magic and the key that will unlock the meaning of life…*

*

After taking another day to rehumanise, I ask Eliza to please order me a taxi into town. Seemingly by chance, Dennis, the taxi driver who picked me up from the airport, is waiting for me outside. He smiles and laughs when he sees me.

'*Buenos días*, my friend,' he says. 'We are meet each other again.' Dennis is wearing the same short-sleeve button-up shirt and cream-coloured fedora. 'You are looking much more healthy already today compare to when I pick you up before.'

'Gracias amigo,' I say, sliding into the front passenger seat and wedging my daypack between my legs. Dennis pulls a U-turn then chugs along up the road with his window rolled down.

'How long you is stay for in Cusco?' he asks.

'About one month. Then I'm going to Iquitos.'

Dennis laughs. 'You are go to *Iquitos*? I love Iquitos, man. Iquitos is a such crazy place.' He turns to smile and nod towards me with infectious enthusiasm. 'You can get some crazy drinks in the jungle, man. They are made from the jungle plants. They have a such good names. They are in a Spanish, the names, but when you translate to English, they are so funny. There is one drink is name: *I meet you on the floor.*' He cracks up laughing as soon as he says it, and I laugh too. I wasn't expecting him to tell me about jungle *party* drugs. 'Another one,' he says, making this cheeky face, 'is called: *Seven times and still I no want to stop!*' He laughs again. 'I bought two of these ones for my wife.' And we both crack up.

The Plaza de Armas swarms with taxi drivers, school children, tourists, locals and dogs. The morning air is cold and biting: thin with oxygen but thick with exhaust fumes, and pierced with car horns, police whistles, stray dog yelps, church bells, jackhammers and crackling dance music. The hills that encircle the city of Cusco are littered with construction sites, just as Eliza had said.

In the least touristy-looking café I could find at short notice, a waiter with jet-black hair and a smooth face takes down my order.

'*Hola amigo,*' I say. '*Ahh, una jugo de piña, y maté de coca, y ahh, agua sin gas, por favor.*'

Fucking fluent.

It doesn't look like I'm going to get my drinks anytime soon, so I drift off to the fantasy world of my last year of high school teaching. I'd been working short-term contracts at this school in the suburbs of Perth on and off for a couple of years before the principal with the sharp suit and sharp haircut finally offered me a full-time contract. But I turned him down. Everyone thought I was a fool when I asked to be a relief teacher for one term instead.

Everyone except Mr Jim Swanson, that is.

I didn't think much of Jim at first. He had a firm handshake, Boston accent, goatee, short curly hair, woollen vest, and a backpack full of maths books. He kept in pretty good shape for an old guy and truth-be-told, just looked to me like a normal, straight-edge, fifty-something-year-old square. But one morning, early in the school year, when I'd skipped the staff briefing and prayer and snuck upstairs to the open-plan office, I found Jim sitting alone at his desk watching the Pink Floyd *Live in Pompeii* concert on his laptop. The school had one of those open plan staff rooms with different subject areas mixed together, and Jim and I had been assigned workstations next to each other. I gave him a little upturn of my chin before I sat down. Jim pulled out his headphones.

'You don't feel like sitting through the briefing this morning either?' he said.

'I don't really get into the whole prayers and singing thing.'

'You know what, Nick? I turn up to school ready to seize the day, and then the goddamn morning briefing just sucks the life outta me.'

'So, you're into Pink Floyd?'

'Oh yeah, buddy, big time.'

And that was enough to get us going.

Jim and I reeled through all the classic albums that'd left a lasting impression on us until Jim said he used to be into the Grateful Dead when he was a young man back in the States. I figured I'd probe a little because to me, a *Deadhead* meant LSD.

'So, does that mean you like, got into that whole *scene?*'

'Those were the times, man.'

We scanned the staffroom to check we were still alone. The faint echo of hymns drifted up from the stairwell.

'What about you, Nick? Do you get into that kinda stuff?'

I nodded. Though my first experiences with DMT were still a year away at this stage, I explained to Jim that I was experienced with weed and MDMA and had tried acid a few times, but that it wasn't until my mate Harry had returned from

18

South America that I started seriously researching psychedelic plants.

'Ayahuasca in Peru,' said Jim. 'Your friend is hardcore.'

'Yeah, just ask him.'

Jim chuckled.

I peered my head around the corner to check if any other teachers were listening. 'Jim, I get the feeling that there's so much more going on around us that we're not aware of. Only no-one around here seems to give a shit.'

'Hey, you know who I think you'd like?'

'Who's that?'

'He's this guy, a bit of an underground hero in the eighties and nineties. His name's Terence McKenna.'

'Mate. I love Terence McKenna!'

And that's how me and Jim Swanson, the fifty-year old maths teacher with a goatee, became friends.

*

The waiter with the jet-black hair and the smooth face arrives with my agua sin gas and my jugo de piña but not my maté de coca. *Donde es mi fucken maté de coca, Señor?*

*

Jim Swanson and I made a regular habit of exchanging books and albums and links to Terence McKenna lectures. We'd whisper to each other about wild experiences – if nothing else, it helped to cut through the tedium of school – though we were always careful not to let the others hear what we were saying.

One morning, I handed Jim a USB stick full of albums from Tool, Mastodon, Karnivool and The Sword. The next day he rolled in late with a big grin on his face, and then he handed me a USB stick full of Yes, Grateful Dead, Pink Floyd and Black Sabbath. That afternoon, Jim and I cracked open a few beers at our desk. Most of the other staff had left for the day so I was blaring an old King Crimson album from my laptop.

'You don't have to be getting home, Jim?'

'It's my wife's turn to make dinner, so there's no rush.'

I took a sip from my beer. 'What's it like having kids?'

'Oh man,' he said, running his hand through his rapidly thinning, though still curly hair. 'There's no quick answer to that one.'

I shrugged. 'I've got nowhere to be.'

'Well let me think then. Honestly dude, it's hard work. I gotta think about parenting all the time. I gotta think about what kinda people my kids are becoming. My wife says I'm too hard on them, and maybe she's right.'

'How so?'

'The way I discipline them. I'm always the bad guy. I dunno, maybe I'm just an asshole sometimes. But they spend too much time on their devices, and I'm only trying to help. I love my kids, man. My two boys. They're smart, and funny as hell. Jesus, they crack me up sometimes.'

'Do you reckon you're a different person now because of your kids?'

'Yeah, sure, but you know, I'm a different person every day anyway.'

'Me too, I guess.'

'Let me put it another way for ya. I *have* to come in here to work. I don't have a choice anymore because I've got a family to provide for. It's not like my life was *over* when my wife gave birth to our first child. But it changed completely. For the first time in my life, I was responsible for another human being. It's beautiful, man, but look, you can't ever really be prepared for it, just try to make sure it's what you really want to do.'

Maybe one day, I thought, then took a long gulp from my beer.

The waiter finally arrives with my coca tea, and I think about one of the last conversations I had with Jim. I was all over the place, not sure whether to accept the principal's offer and finally 'establish' myself at the school or cut my ties and run for the jungle.

'Look Nick,' Jim said to me. 'The way I see it you've got two options. You accept this teaching gig with all its flaws and limitations and you commit to it and you quit complaining about it every day. Or you pack your bags and get the hell outta here. I can see it in your face that you know what you have to do. No point denying it. You've got that look about you. I watch you tapping your feet away here all day. You're gonna give me a stroke just watching you. You've gotta get *out* there, buddy. Have an adventure. There's a long time before you need to worry about settling down in a job. This is *your* time. This kind of opportunity doesn't stick around forever. One day you'll have two kids and wonder what the hell happened to your life.'

*

After strolling listlessly around Cusco for a while, stopping regularly to catch my breath and becoming somewhat intentionally lost, I ask for directions to the San Pedro markets. Outside in the sunshine I find vendors displaying fruits and vegetables atop coloured fabrics on the concrete floors or on trestle tables as businessmen, children, couples and tourists wander past, eating fried potato snacks or smoking cigarettes.

Inside is dark except for the areas that are neon lit. The floors are dusty and black and there are endless lanes of wares: tapestries, trinkets, beanies and scarves, wooden sculptures, shoes and ties, leather bags, sacks of rice and buckets of cheese.

Locals populate the dining section. They sit on simple wooden benches in rows out the front of each eatery. The fried chicken vendors seem to be the most popular, but you can get roast chicken, chicken soup, fried fish and rice, or if you're game, beef gristle, tripe and offal soup. I order what I hope is vegetable soup. A local couple smile when I sit next to them.

'*Hola amigos*,' I say with an upturn of my chin.

I slurp down my soup, then retreat to The Sanctuary.

I've been emailing back and forth for a few weeks with a woman named Isabella. She works at Way of the Spirit Healing Centre in Iquitos. Isabella recently took over as office manager at the centre from a young Australian guy called Will. Strange as it seems, three different acquaintances of mine from three different social circles told me to get in touch with this Will character.

The first of these encounters was at a pub in Perth. I was chatting with my friend's husband, and he mentioned his San Pedro cactus was about ready to harvest. I said I'd never tried San Pedro, but I was planning to head to Peru to search for ayahuasca. My friend's husband said he went to school with a guy who was managing a retreat centre in Peru, and he gave me Will's contact details.

A month later I visited Melbourne for a wedding. Before long I was snorting cocaine and drinking beers with a friend I hadn't seen since he moved east. I told him about my plans for South America, and it turned out he'd gone to university with Will. My ex-girlfriend Jessica was at the wedding as well, and I embarrassed myself terribly by collapsing into a pot plant at some stage during the night. She texted after the party to check if I was okay.

Later that summer while drinking a cold beer after a long day on the cricket field, I got to talking with the captain of my team. He mentioned he'd spent a week in Peru drinking ayahuasca during the Australian winter. I asked him where he stayed, and of course, he said Way of the Spirit. But by the time I'd followed up on these synchronicities, Will had moved on to begin his training with a master ayahuascero, somewhere deeper in the Amazon jungle, and Isabella had taken over his job.

Back in my room at The Sanctuary, I fill out Isabella's form, attach it to an email, click send then lie down on my back on my bed and stare blankly at the ceiling.

*

Email Subject: Re: Way of the Spirit Healing Centre – Questionnaire

Hi Isabella

Thanks for getting back to me again so promptly. Yes, my friends and I are keen for a triple-share house to ourselves, that sounds perfect! Stan and Billy are both happy with ten days. I'd like to extend my stay to fourteen if that's possible?

Below are my responses to the questions you sent. I sent the questions to Stan and Billy, so they should be coming through to you soon. I'm currently in Cusco; the others are still in Perth. I'll keep you posted on my movements. Please let me know if you need any more info.

Cheers
Nick

Way of the Spirit Healing Centre – New Guest Questionnaire

How old are you?
27
Are you married; do you have children?
Not married, no kids
What do you do for work?
I currently work as a high school teacher
Do you have a past history of, or currently suffer from any of the following:
Cardiovascular disease, including heart attacks;
High / low blood pressure;
Mental illness;
Recent surgery;
Past or recent physical injuries (fractures or dislocations);
Glaucoma;
Retinal detachment;
Recent or current infectious or communicable diseases;
Epilepsy;
Asthma;
Diabetes (Type 1 or 2);
Other - including symptoms that affect: head/neck; eyes, ears, nose or throat; lungs; skin; intestines / bowels / digestion; back; bladder or kidneys; chest / heart; circulation; ability to sleep.
Comments:
None of the above.

Are you currently taking any type of medications? If so, please list all medications including dosage and frequency taken.

No medication.

Have you ever taken tranquilising medications, SSRIs or any other antidepressant medication? If yes, when and for how long?

Yes. I took SSRIs for depression for 18 months. I stopped about 3 years ago.

Please list any allergies:

Hay fever. Dust (mild).

Have you ever had any type of seizure?

No.

Have you ever been hospitalised for medical reasons?

No.

Have you ever been hospitalised for psychiatric reasons?

No.

Do you have any history whatsoever of psychosis, schizophrenia, hallucinations or bi-polar diagnosis?

No.

Are you currently in therapy or involved in any type of support group?

No.

Is there anything else about your physical or emotional health that we should be aware of?

Nothing comes to mind at this stage.

List any recreational substances that you have taken over the past 12 months. (Including alcohol and marijuana). Please include frequency of use.

Alcohol (3–4 times per week); Marijuana (once a month); MDMA (once every couple of months); LSD (2 times per year); Cocaine (2 times per year); DMT (twice).

Please describe any experience that you have had with regards to Amazonian plant medicine.

None.

Do you have a spiritual practice?

Not really. I grew up in a secular household but went to a religious high school. I never developed a spiritual practice, but I would like to start one, I think.

Are you comfortable in solitude and silent introspection? (Please note undergoing a plant diet often involves being in isolation for varying lengths of time).

Very comfortable.

Please state your personal reasons for your interest in our program. It is helpful for us to know your intention and aspirations with plant medicines.

Personal growth and exploration. I'd like to develop greater self-awareness and self-control.

Confront potentially repressed memories and discover the root causes to my anxiety and depression. I've been through a process of therapy and anti-depressant medication, but I don't believe I've resolved the underlying issues.

Develop a greater and more profound level of spirituality in my life.

Connect with other intelligences and explore other realms & dimensions

Also, I'd like to figure out what to do with my life because I feel lost.

Are you willing to undertake this journey with full commitment?

Yes.

Chapter Three
Urubamba

In central Cusco we become stuck behind a marching band. My taxi driver pulls over into a side-street and explains that he needs to collect someone from a hostel down the road, then he disappears into the crowd. I step out of the car to stretch my legs and bite my fingernails. The air is thick with the smoke of barbecued meats and firecrackers. Two tiny Peruvian students dressed in traditional garments slip past holding hands. I wave to them and say, 'Hola' and they giggle and skip away.

Lucio and Ariana, the mestizo ayahuasceros that Harry recommended, arranged for this driver to pick me up from The Sanctuary and deliver me to their house in Urubamba for the weekend. I spent my remaining days at The Sanctuary drinking coca tea, writing, stretching on the floor and hyperventilating. I journaled in my room, or sometimes out in the backyard under a shady tree, listening to the birds singing, or the chainsaws screaming. Eliza took great care of me. She gave me books to read and soup to eat. She asked about my intentions and my family, and she advised me on ayahuasca. But despite her nurturing, my existence continued to be a fog of jetlag, altitude sickness, confusion and anxiety. Confusion about what the hell I was doing in Peru. Anxiety about what the hell was going to happen to me this weekend at the ayahuasca retreat.

After fifteen minutes, the driver and the traveller emerge from the crowd. The traveller is a young woman with long black hair, animated brown eyes and a smattering of freckles on her lustrous though guarded face. I join her in the backseat and introduce myself. Her name is Marie.

'Are you Brazilian?' I ask, having recognised her accent.

'I am.' She smiles. Our driver pulls out from the side of the road and narrowly misses a gang of street-dogs. 'Have you been to Brazil?'

'No, but I'm friends with a lot of Brazilians from when I worked in a bar.'

'You're Australian, right?'

'Yes. I'm from Perth. Have you been?'

'I've lived in Sydney for the past three years.'

'What brought you to Australia?'

'My boyfriend is Australian.'

Ouch. Conscious not to let my disappointment show, I keep the conversation moving. Marie and I talk about travelling the world and inevitably, about ayahuasca and other psychedelics.

'I just sense that ayahuasca is the key to sorting me out,' I say. 'There's something wrong with me but I don't know what it is. I feel like I've lost something from when I was a child. I can't really connect with anything. And I feel there's this big, golden ball of power inside me, waiting to be unleashed into the world. I just have to figure out how to do it.'

Marie smiles nervously then gazes out her window.

I might've overdone it with all the 'golden ball of power' stuff.

It's over an hour before we get to Urubamba. Along the way we had to stop three times for herds of sheep to cross the road. The last of the herds had no shepherd, not even a dog to guide them. Now the driver parks on a dusty side street flanked by crumbling cream walls. We get out of the car, and I scan the surroundings. In each direction, tall hills rise and grow into mountains sprouting with shrubs and trees and littered with boulders. The sun is fierce, yet the air is cold and biting and thin. No-one is willing to acknowledge it, but we are alone out here. These streets are deserted. A bead of grimy, salty sweat slides down from my brow to the cracked skin of my lips. The butterflies in my stomach whip themselves up into a frenzy. *I've made a mistake*, I think.

But a tall, slender man emerges from behind a slowly opening electric gate, and my shoulders relax.

'Hello,' says the tall man, grinning widely and baring a mouthful of small, crooked teeth. 'I am Lucio.'

'Hi Lucio, I'm Nick. Nice to meet you.'

We shake hands. Lucio is long-limbed, with long black hair, a patchy dark beard and kind, squinty little eyes. He looks like a stoned Peruvian Jesus.

'Is a pleasure to meet,' he says softly. 'Welcome to my house. Please, come.' Lucio opens his palm and invites Marie and me to enter the property. A light gravel pathway leads through well-kept lawns and past flowering fruit trees to a paved courtyard where a scruffy yellow dog lies bathing his belly in the sun. The courtyard is encircled by more fruit trees and low-lying flower beds, and pots with cacti. From the centre of the courtyard, an enclosed dining hall stands to the left, and to the right, looms the main house, a two-storey structure of wood and brick and glass. A small hand-crafted waterfall cascades in the courtyard and over the outer walls of the property. Away in the distance, a line of mountains marks the boundary of the Sacred Valley. Lucio leads us through the main house, pointing out the kitchen with its thick wooden table-top and hanging pots and pans. Opposite the kitchen is the ceremony room, veiled by soft white curtains. My belly tightens. Upstairs, Lucio shows Marie to her room and then leads me to mine. I lie down on my bed and try to relax in preparation for the night ahead, though my thoughts drift inevitably to the past.

While I was disengaged a lot at high school, I do remember being particularly attentive in Health class when the teacher handed out drug information pamphlets. They were supposed to deter us but to me they were like toy catalogues. There was one for opiates, stimulants and depressants, but the one that really piqued my curiosity was called 'hallucinogens'. I didn't know much about them at the time, but I knew immediately and with complete clarity that one day I would discover what these mysterious drugs were all about. I'm not sure why I was so interested. But something about the power of a drug to change the way the world looked fascinated me. Maybe it was because I had imaginary friends growing up. Maybe it's because my sister and I used to find fairies in the bush near our house. Maybe it's because I spent most of my childhood staring into imaginary realms. Maybe it's because I wanted to believe that reality could be more than the mundane world I was faced with.

*

The ceremony space opposite the kitchen is partially unveiled to reveal the temple within. I slip off my shoes and step through the break in the drapes. There's a young fair-skinned couple inside already. I smile towards them then select a mat wedged into a corner on the opposite side of the room. A plastic bucket sits ominously beside my mat. Marie enters the room, and I soften when she chooses the mat to my right. I hadn't noticed him before, but in a dark corner sits a solemn Peruvian man. To his left is a door to the bathroom. Lucio and his wife Ariana share a mat and a blanket, and they sit against the wall opposite the entrance. Ariana has a white woollen jumper on. Her face is golden, and her hair is long and curled. A few candles flicker in front of the couple, providing the only light in the room.

When the rest of the guests have chosen a mat, Lucio begins to pray. He thanks Pachamama for the medicine then he falls silent, and we sit and wait. The knot in my stomach tightens. The energy in the room is prickly. Something is off.

I try to convince myself that it's only nerves.

I think of the DMT Realm opening a portal in Stan's backyard. The exploding plants. The Language! And oh goodness, the Horror!

I know I'm becoming attached to outcome, but I just want so desperately for a beautiful vision tonight. I want to meet Terence McKenna's self-transforming machine-elves. I want to meet God. I want to have adventures with beautiful feminine jungle spirits. I want to go back in time and live as an Egyptian Pharaoh. I want a vision for my future. I want to know my purpose here on Earth. I want to know what's wrong with me so I can cure it and move on with my life.

I want to understand why I'm so terribly sad all the time.

One by one, Lucio calls us up to accept the ayahuasca. When he calls my name, I rise from my mat and sit cross-legged before him and Ariana.

'How do you feel, Nicholas?' asks Lucio.

'Calm.' I mean nervous.

Lucio pours the ayahuasca from a large plastic bottle into a small wooden cup. I bring the cup to my face. The smell is thick and sour fermenting compost. Rotten dirt. My heartbeat thumps in my stomach. Lucio and Ariana wait silently.

Please, let me have a beautiful vision tonight.

I touch the cup to my lips and pour the liquid into my mouth. The taste is bitter and confronting. Earthy, sour, rich sediment. I hold for a moment so I don't gag. Then I swallow. It takes great effort not to cough and splutter.

'*Gracias*,' I whisper, holding out the cup for Lucio. He takes it, and I make the symbol for prayer at my chest and nod to him and then to Ariana, and then I stand and slowly shuffle back to my mat.

It is done.

After waiting an hour or so, Lucio invites anyone who would like a second cup to approach. Some of the others are tripping already. Some are moaning softly, and others are purging into their buckets. I can't feel anything besides the knot in my stomach, so I rise to my feet in the darkness and shuffle over to Lucio and Ariana to ask for another cup. Afterwards, the mestizo ayahuasceros sing, and they pray. The people around me purge. I try to concentrate on meditating, but nothing happens. I sit cross-legged until my knees scream with pain and then I lie down and toss around through long, tedious hours of nothing. My back aches and my neck is tense, and there's a growing, swelling, bloating in my stomach.

This is so shit.

I think of Harry. The prick.

What the fuck did he get me into?

After an age of boredom and resentful thoughts, Lucio speaks a final prayer to close the ceremony. It's only now that I begin to feel something from the ayahuasca. A heavy force presses down on me, pushing me into the ground. I close my eyes and roll over to face the wall. Fear drives a stake into my belly and sews my mouth shut. I hold back the tears that are trying to burst through.

Candles are lit and the others begin to whisper. There's talk of visions and amazement. I curl tighter, choking on shame and disappointment. Thirty tortuous minutes pass like this; silently wrestling the shadowy force nailing me down, while the others giggle and sigh like fucking schoolgirls.

I muster the strength to stand up, and trudge out of the ceremony room, frustrated and nauseous, up the steps to my bedroom.

Now I am alone and behind my closed eyelids swarms a precession of grotesque metallic organisms. Writhing and filthy, a horde of gigantic rusty squirming maggots. They are sharp, spiked, barbed, and they fold into one another. Repulsive and frightening. *I hate this!* I am silently weeping, mouth agape. Swirling dark fractals, now. Metallic intertwining snakes. Confusing and wicked. Black and grey H.R. Giger ghouls. Nightmarish reptilian metal monsters and crawling insects and penetration of the skin. All the while, the terrible pain in my stomach worsens, as though a goblin is stretching me from the inside.

Have I been poisoned? Maybe I should go to the bathroom?

But people will hear me if I go to the bathroom. They're all happy and I am disgusting.

A voice speaks: *This is a lesson, Nicholas. This is part of the cleaning process. Your reluctance to purge is a blockage. Don't hold it in.*

The Giger monsters seem to have settled, for now. I drag my body to the bathroom, sit on the toilet and piss out of my arse. A torrential spray of nasty liquid, like the lukewarm leftovers of a microwave curry noodle soup, rapidly flees from my body.

I hold my head in my hands for a few moments and gently cry.

After washing my hands, I dart back to the toilet bowl to vomit. The purge comes freely; a frothy black cloud pouring out of my body. Little twirling black feathers twist their way out of my mouth. Each are raven's claws that once held something in my stomach. Now they are gone. I return to bed with a stomach cramp but soon fall asleep.

*

On the grass outside I sit alone in the cold morning sunshine. The air is thin in Urubamba, and fumes from nearby construction sites waft over the stone walls. I ate breakfast this morning in silence, listening to the others share stories of incredible visions from last night. I felt like crying at the dining table. I roll a blob of sunscreen down my arm and the smell sparks a wave of nostalgia. I'm slopping on sunscreen as a boy. Mum is wearing a tennis skirt and a visor, and her arms are tanned. Her hands are greasy with sweat, and I see the veins running over her bones. She's smiling but she isn't happy. Dad's arms are hairy, and he smells salty. The white of the sunscreen collects by his hair follicles and the sweat forms little beads of creamy moisture.

I'm in Grade 4, and my parents are fighting all the time. My first love, Megan O'Neil, dumps me and I want to die. Now my parents live in separate houses and only Mum goes to the tennis club. I'm playing dodge with the boys and I don't know why they try so hard to hurt each other with the tennis ball. I'm struck in the belly and want to vomit. I'm sitting in a small booth, listening for sounds, and have to press a button when I hear a particular beep. A doctor pokes holes into my ear drums, so the fluid can drain out. I'm walking home from school, busting to go to the toilet but don't make it. I piss my pants, and when I get home, with a grinding ball of shame in my stomach, I lie to my mum and tell her the neighbours had their sprinklers on and I got caught. She just says, 'Oh dear, that was unlucky,' and takes my shorts, puts them in the wash and tells me to have a shower.

Marie glides out from the dining room, waves to me and approaches. She is gorgeous. *I don't think I can handle this right now.* I affect a smile. 'How's it going?'

'I'm great.' She sits on the grass next to me. 'How are you, Nick?'

'I'm okay.' *Don't cry in front of her.* 'How was your night?'

'So beautiful. It was –' she pauses to search for the words. 'It was something very special. I felt so *held* for the whole ceremony. My grandmother was there with me, wrapping me up in blankets and holding my head in her lap. She sang to me, like when I was a child, and she rocked me gently. I was a little scared later when there were snakes all around. One rose to look straight into my eyes. But my grandmother held me and reassured me. I'm so happy.'

I want to die.

'How was your ceremony?' she asks.

I turn away. 'It was difficult. I didn't have any visions until I was lying in my bed. And then, they were very… dark.'

'I'm sorry.'

I shake my head. 'I've been locked in a spiral of sad memories.'

'Sad memories?'

She is radiant. I am a pit of despair. 'Memories from when I was a kid. Like, I remember being at the beach with my mother and sister and seeing a group of kids from my school and I'm so shy and anxious and awkward that I hide under my towel, and all I want in this world is to disappear into nothingness.' I notice the words flooding out of my mouth but I'm powerless to reign them in.

'Childhood is strange,' she says. 'This life is so strange.'

Marie says she's going to take a shower, and I imagine her naked body for a moment but then it's just me on the grass again in my pit of despair. I'm so goddamn lonely. Marie is lovely, but I don't want to talk to her anymore. She thinks I'm a weirdo. I am an outsider. I am disconnected, nervous, weak, alone, small.

I stand up and pace the perimeter of the property.

Fuck you, Harry. You piece of shit. The ayahuasca didn't work. Everyone else had amazing visions except me. What am I even doing here? I shouldn't have come by myself. This was a mistake. Fuck! Why did I come alone? Why would I put myself in this goddamn situation? How could I possibly think I'd be able to cope here? I am trapped in this place. There's not enough room here. I need to be in open spaces. I can't handle it here. Jesus. I can't trust myself. Not in this emotional state. I'm fucken losing it. This is gonna go bad! I just know it. I'm —

Stop! Nick, please mate, calm yourself. This is a challenge. Get through it. Learn from it.

I circle back to my original spot on the grass.

You're right.

I walk back inside the main house and to the bathroom upstairs. A shower helps to reset my emotions, and to wash away some of the sadness and some of the anxiety and shame. I tread downstairs and out through the sliding door to the courtyard. Birds swoop in and out of the water fountain. Bees hover around the flowers of the fruit trees. I notice the green on the tops of the trees on the mountainside. The other travellers are in the dining room already, preparing for lunch.

It's gonna be alright, mate. You're tender right now but that's okay.

In the dining room, the long wooden table is adorned with garden salads, roasted vegetables, pumpkin soup and fruits. I slowly slide a chair out from under the table and sit down gingerly like I've got some kind of crippling illness. A sip from my coca tea helps to soften my heart just a little. *These are good people. They had beautiful experiences last night. Why not be happy for them?*

I take another sip from my coca tea and feel much better. I am ready for the ceremony tonight.

*

In the darkness, I drink the brew then sit and wait. The others moan and shuffle and purge. Lucio and Ariana sing, and they pray, and they purge.

A second cup.

A plea to ayahuasca.

But nothing happens.

It's just more goddamn bitter disappointment. No visions, no insight, no aliens, no God. No waterfalls or jungles or deserts or dancing machine elves. There're not even the goddamn H.R. Giger monsters. At this stage I'd rather the Horror than nothing.

Lucio lights the candles, and I know it's all over. The others begin to whisper. Some are laughing. I hold back my tears and whisper goodnight in Marie's direction through trembling lips.

In the bathroom I force myself to vomit, then wash my body and curl into bed.

Chapter Four
Ollantaytambo

Lucio's draped in white linens and his face is solemn. We're at the dining table. The others are outside in the sunshine, waiting for their turn to debrief.

'I don't know how to interpret what happened, Lucio. I didn't have a visionary experience. There was no guidance. My friend Harry said that—'

'People come here, and they want the big visions. This is not the purpose of the medicine. Our purpose here is to clean.' Lucio speaks slowly, considering each word as though he is carefully sculpting it before letting it sail out into the world. I'm trying my best not to cry. 'I recommend for you a practice of meditation. It does not matter which practice you choose, the important thing is to practice. Something for the body, and for the heart, and for the mind.'

It takes all my energy to generate a smile. 'Thank you, Lucio.'

'This is my pleasure, Nick.'

I rise from my chair, and we hug, then I trudge upstairs to pack my bags. While I understand what Lucio said, I still feel cheated. Not by Lucio, Ariana, or ayahuasca, but rather by the universe itself. Despite all my careful planning, this first part of my journey has been a failure.

The others are heading back to Cusco this morning but I'm making my own way to Ollantaytambo, having decided back in Perth that a few more days in the Sacred Valley after the ayahuasca ceremonies would be better for my integration than returning straight to Cusco. We take a group photo, standing in front of the fountain in the courtyard with the mountain in the background. I hug each of the travellers, even the solemn Peruvian man, and linger especially long during my hug with Marie. I thank Lucio and Ariana one last time and then hop into the front seat of my taxi.

'*Hola amigo. Mi nombre es Nick.*'

'Pablo.' We shake hands. '*Habla Español?*'

'Ahh, no not really. *Solo un poco.* Do you speak English?'

'No,' he says, grinning. So, we resign ourselves to sitting in silence. Which is fine with me. I am no longer a person. I am a hollow shell.

As we approach the outskirts of Ollantaytambo, Pablo slows and eventually parks the car on the side of the road. He looks uneasy. Pablo mutters something to himself then gets out of the car and wanders off down the road.

Um. What the fuck, Pablo?

He walks over to the opposite side of the road and takes a piss against a tree. When he's finished pissing, he walks a little further down the road and stands looking at something ahead. A young boy chases a pig down the road, but Pablo keeps his eyes ahead.

When he returns, I ask, '*Problemo?*'

'*Policia.*'

'*Policia es problemo para tú?*'

I understand only fragments of his reply. Pablo drives slowly on ahead. At a police check-point, a moustached officer lowers his head to lock eyes with Pablo through the open window of the taxi. The two men argue. Pablo points to me. I smile to the officer. The officer shakes his finger. Pablo hangs his head. The policeman waves us through and Pablo grins.

Pablo drops me off in the main square of town. There's a modest central park, with stone pathways, stray dogs, benches, flower beds and small patches of grass. Old ladies with long plaited hair and bowler hats sit on the sidewalk, draped in fabrics, with mandarins and bags of salted corn laid out before them. A modest church built of stone and wood rises in one wing, and along the rest of the square stand various overpriced restaurants, trinket shops, tour group offices and clothing stores. A steady flow of taxis circle and as I haul my backpack from Pablo's car, a large bus swings around the square and heads off towards another town with a full load of tourists. I take a deep breath then grasp my phone from my pocket and use my offline map of Ollantaytambo to guide me down a side alley and along a grey cobblestone path to the old part of town.

At my hotel, the girl at the front desk shows me to my studio room. A window opens out to a communal balcony with views of the site of Ollantaytambo. The walls are a light pastel colour and seem to lean in towards me on all sides. When the girl leaves, I throw my bags onto the floor, collapse onto my bed and cry.

*

I need help. I need to talk to someone.

It's one in the morning in Perth; my mother and sister will be asleep for sure.

I check the time in London. Seven in the evening.

Should I call her?

She doesn't want to hear from you, you fucking loser!

Bit harsh, mate.

I send a text. Five minutes later, "Jessica" flashes on my phone and I swipe to answer.

'Hello,' I mumble.

'Hey Nicky, how are you?'

I can't manage any more words. I take a deep breath and just wheeze into the phone.

'I had a feeling something was wrong,' she says.

Jessica lets me splutter and sob for a while.

'This is all part of it,' she says. 'You know that, Nicky. Just remember that you're on an adventure. This is one of the hard parts of your adventure, but soon you'll be out of this and back on your feet.' There's a pause. 'You know that you are loved, Nicky.'

My eyes well again, but I'm smiling. 'Thanks, Jess. I really appreciate it.'

'You can call me anytime.'

'Thanks.'

She is just so lovely.

Yeah, you really fucked that one up didn't you?

…Nope. Block it out. Don't even go there.

I rise from the bed and begin to unpack, hanging some worn shirts onto the hat rack, laying out my shoes on the floor and rearranging a few sections of clothes. Breathing is painful. I've been opened and exposed like a gutted fish.

After just a few minutes it appears the walls have inched closer while I wasn't paying attention. I lie back down on the floor and do that kind of choke-sobbing thing you do when you really need to cry but also you don't want the people in the next room to hear so you end up making snorting farm animal sounds and runny snot shoots out of your nose and drool runs out of your mouth all over your clothes.

*

I float along in the cool air of the Sacred Valley from the hotel to the main square in search of food. This is not the good kind of floating like when you've just started a new romance, this is the kind of floating where your body feels hollow, drained of all substance. After a lap of the main square, I take a punt on a small, quiet diner. I need something simple because right now my stomach is coiled into a terrible knot and my organs are clawing themselves viciously. A young woman with long black hair tied into a ponytail, tight blue jeans and a loose-fitting t-shirt takes my order. My vegetable soup comes out looking a little like what I served up into the toilet bowl after the ayahuasca ceremonies in Urubamba. The woman sits back at her table with a notepad and a calculator.

A long-haired gringo with a backpack slung over his shoulder bustles in, panting. 'Do you guys have beers?' he asks with an unmistakable Australian twang.

'*Cerveza*,' I mutter from behind my bowl of soup.

'What's that buddy?'

'*Cerveza* means beer.'

'Cheers mate.' He turns back to the girl and asks, 'Do you guys have *cervezas*?'

42

In my hotel room I sit at the little side table and stare out the window at the ruins of Ollantaytambo. A couple pass by my window, walking arm in arm. I realise I am alone in this world and crumple down into a heap on the floor.

By the time I pull myself together again it's dark outside and I'm lying on the floor spooning a tear-soaked pillow, haunted by an image of a white-haired boy standing in the corner of a room. I can't be sure if it's a memory or a projection. I kind of hope there's some brutal memory of childhood trauma I've repressed that's waiting to be uncovered from the shadows. At least then I'd have a reason for feeling this way.

A few years ago, when I decided to stop taking antidepressants, I convinced myself that I was willing to take the emotional lows if it meant I had a chance to experience the beauty of the world again. Surely that was better than being utterly numb. I'm not so sure anymore. Because right now, I don't want to be here. I don't want to live in this world.

Maybe I should just finally kill myself and be done with it.

How would I do it, I wonder? Jump off a bridge? Bullet in the head? Overdose? No. I'm not the kind of person who would actually go through with it. You need a real capacity for violence and a kind of robust certitude to end your own life. This is different. I've never quite been able to convey the feeling to someone who hasn't experienced it for themselves. I don't want to kill myself. I just don't want to be here anymore. I don't want to be alive. I want to go to sleep tonight and never wake up again. It's just not worth it, this life. There's no point to any of it. It doesn't make a difference what I do.

We are all fucked.

I blow my nose into a sacrificial shirt and take a few deep breaths, then muster up some of the fragments of a smile. It wasn't always like this. I was happy once. I know I was. The world was magical when I was a child. I used to play dress-ups with my sister, and we'd put on plays for the whole family. I was happy then, wasn't I? So, what happened? That time of my life is murky. I know that I would just shut down for days or even weeks at a time. Mum was the only one who could get me to talk. She'd take me and the dog for long walks in the bush. That was her way of opening me up so we could connect.

That's it. I know what I have to do. It'll be better tomorrow morning. If I can just make it through the night.

*

The cold morning air stings my nostrils as I stride through the dark grey cobblestone grid of lanes making up the old part of town. All the buildings have Inca foundations of solid black stone blocks that fit together without mortar. On top of the foundations sit the Spanish colonial architecture of whitewashed brick walls and wooden frames. Numerous earthquakes have hit the Sacred Valley since the Spanish conquered the Inca Empire but each time, the Inca foundations remain standing, and the Spanish-built parts collapse.

A handful of keen travellers pass by, along with a few bleary-eyed locals and a couple of dogs sniffing each other's butts. I reach an innocuous opening in the outer wall with steps leading to higher ground. Upwards I clamber under overhanging branches, until, emerging out above the line of the highest buildings of the old part of town, I can just make out the ruined Ollantaytambo, still cloaked in shade beyond the town and the river offshoot.

Ahead on the path, a man with long brown hair rolling out from under his baseball cap and a cigarette tucked behind his ear, is bent over and coughing.

'How's it going there, mate?' he calls out. He's wearing a skate-brand singlet, boardshorts, and has a dirty little moustache. 'This fucken altitude, ay?'

'You're the guy from the diner yesterday.'

'What's that, buddy?' he says, cocking his head.

'You asked for beer, and I said it's called *cerveza*.'

'No shit. You're right! I'm Craig.'

'Nick,' I say, holding out my hand.

We shake and Craig says, 'Hey, so feel free to pass me, dude. Or if you don't mind waiting a bit 'til I've caught my breath, we can climb this thing together?'

A friend…

Craig and I spend the next hour and a half tracking different paths across the hill. At mid-morning, we sit and eat mandarins and bananas and watch the sun hit the Ollantaytambo ruin for the first time. The site was built at the base of the mountain's jutting edge. In its prime the construction may well have wrapped all the way around the edge, but now it climbs up only the side that catches the mid-morning sun. There would've been buildings and walls and roofs at some stage but now there's just a series of steps leading up to nowhere. It looks like the steps have been cut for a giant.

Craig passes me a flimsy joint, and I take a few drags then lie down on my back on a small patch of grass.

'So, Nicko, what brings you out this way?'

I spin around into a cross-legged seat. 'A number of things, really.' I usually hold off discussing psychedelics with people I've just met, but since Craig rolled the joint, I figure it's safe to share. 'I was just in Urubamba, at a small centre drinking ayahuasca.'

'How was it?'

'I'm still processing but honestly, I didn't have a good experience at all. It's not that it was a bad trip or anything like that, I just didn't get much out of it. The only visions I had were really dark and confusing. It's been getting me down. Yesterday I was super depressed. I feel better today though.'

'Nothing like getting out into nature to figure yourself out.'

The dope makes my pulse race a little, but my heart is warm and expanding. There's still a tight little knot in my belly but I can feel it loosening. Craig says he was supposed to be travelling with his girlfriend, but they broke up over Christmas. As much as I prefer to avoid Australians overseas, Craig and I seem to be on the same wavelength almost immediately. 'I'd already quit my job in Sydney,' he says, 'and booked my plane tickets. So, I figured, fuck it, might as well go on the trip anyway.'

'How's it been travelling on your own?'

'A bit tricky, actually. I haven't really figured out what kind of traveller I am. Am I staying in Airbnb's by myself just reading and writing? Am I a backpacker staying in hostels and partying? Am I looking for a place to live and settle in for longer periods of time? Should I spend my cash, or be super tight with money to make it last for a year? I seem to fluctuate between all of these things, then I realise none of it actually matters and I should just do what makes me happy.'

'So, you're a writer?'

'Nah not really. I've just found that writing my thoughts down in a journal is helping me process the breakup with my ex. Who knows, maybe I'll turn it into a book.'

'That's cool. I'm supposed to be writing a book over here. It's pretty much turned to shit though.'

'How come?'

'I dunno. Things just haven't really gone the way I thought they would.' Wanting to quickly shift the conversation away from my failings even as an *aspiring* writer I say, 'Hey, so do you reckon you'll stick around Cusco for a while?'

'Fuck no,' says Craig. 'Too cold out here for my blood. Nah, I'll be heading up to Central America in a week or so. Cold beers, hot beaches and beautiful women. I'll start off in Mexico, but then I'm meeting a mate in Costa Rica. You should join us.'

I shrug. 'Sounds good to me, but honestly, I have no idea how long I'll end up travelling for. I've been thinking of pulling the pin already.'

'You can't leave now, mate. You're only at the start! Anyway, no pressure about Costa. It's an open invite. Alrighty, speaking of cold beers, it's almost lunchtime. Fancy a *cerveza*?'

Chapter Five
The Wind Gate

Last night, while we were drunk and excited, Craig and I agreed to hike together to the Wind Gate. A round-trip would take all day, according to someone in the bar whose name and face I've forgotten. This is why we're up so goddamn early stocking up on fruits and nuts and water at the market. It's early even for the slumberous locals sipping their coca tea. The women are dressed in long coloured fabric, and they squat behind piles of fresh fruit and vegetables. Children with grubby faces run through the stalls, ducking behind their mothers. A cheerful middle-aged man jams seven different fruits into a machine then hands me and Craig a tall cup each of the frothy liquid.

We set out on the road that begins on the far side of the Urubamba River. The path is well-trodden, flat and dusty, with smatterings of loose stones and donkey shit. The morning air is thin and cold, my lips are dry, and my head is thick, but I'm in good spirits. It's a kind of hangover delirium. I probably shouldn't have gone out drinking last night, as I'm supposed to be keeping to the post-ayahuasca diet, but I'd made a friend and the knot in my stomach had loosened. And this, I felt, was worth celebrating.

Onwards we trek, beyond sight of the ancient ruins of Ollantaytambo, up a steep incline where the vegetation around us is shrubby and spikey and earth-brown. Along each side of the river in both directions is farmland, with little towns or settlements dotted along the way. Beyond the river and the farmland and the little towns tower the mountains of the Sacred Valley, dark green and jagged, and climbing up to peaks crusted with ice. Before long I've stripped off my shirt and am wearing just my shorts and my backpack in the beating sun, with the booze sweating out of my skin.

We carry on like this for another couple of hours before we come across a local Peruvian man in uniform napping under a tree. Craig asks him how much further to the Wind Gate.

'One more hour,' says the man with his hands clasped behind his head.

A chill wind swirls. I retrieve my shirt from my bag and slip it back over my head. Craig finds a soft patch of grass and slumps down.

'That'll do me,' he says. 'You go on ahead, mate. I'll just take a little siesta.'

'You sure?' I say.

'Yeah, dude. Seriously, you go on. I'll wait here. I'm fucken spent.'

Craig tips the peak of his cap over his face and rests his hands under his head. Beyond him, the path back to town disappears over a hill. My body is begging me to give up on the Wind Gate and take a nap in the shade.

But I can't stop now. This would be another failure. And so soon after the last.

I continue the hike alone.

Over the edge of the path to my right is a steep drop-off to the valley and the river and the train line below. Somewhere up ahead, the elusive Wind Gate is still obscured. From yonder down the path come two figures. At first it seems like an apparition but no, it must be real. A donkey leading a llama back into town. I rub my eyes and carry on.

Another hour passes and still, I'm yet to reach the peak. I think of Craig and wonder if he'll stay on that patch of grass or trek home without me. As I climb further, my stomach begins to squelch and stab and claw. A strange pressure drills into my temples and I'm starting to lose control of my limbs. The wind howls at my face, as though it's taunting me: 'Are you going to give up, Gringo?'

Onward I march, steadily towards my destination.

A stone arch appears from behind a cloud of mist at the top of the mountain. I stop to breathe and to drink water. My shirt clings to the sweat on my back. I'm close. I gather my strength for the final push and with a few determined strides I know I'm going to make it. The Wind Gate transforms from a distant mirage to a reality, and I step through the portal into a small open courtyard with perfect views of the meandering Urubamba River below, and beyond, the stunning snow-capped mountains of the Sacred Valley. The view is mesmerising and magical but as saliva pools in the bottom of my mouth, I'm gripped by powerful nausea and blurred vision, and my mood turns from elation to panic. Adrenaline shoots across my body, pushing out sweat from my pores.

I must get to lower ground.

And so down I traverse, dizzy, and anxious that I might lose control of my legs and collapse off the edge of the path to my death. At least it'll be certain death. I won't have to worry about paralysis.

I cover the ground quickly, and at the base of the path, stop at a small set of ruins to catch my breath and survey the situation. It's a recent ruin, the shell of a set of old houses. Horses and cows mill about the place while a sheep dog sleeps in the tall grass. A sharp pain stabs me below my belly button; a clear message from my bowels. I hustle to a secluded corner in one of the busted old rooms of the ruin. I slip one boot off and pull my pants and underwear down and off that leg and then spin them around to rest on my still-booted foot, then squat down on the grass in the corner of the room and do my business. It's an emergency hangover shit, so everything floods out rather rapidly and without fuss. In the top pouch of my backpack is a stash of tissues and bottle of hand sanitiser.

I clean myself up and stand, much relieved, rather amused, and surprised at how much better I feel. I bury the evidence and set off to find Craig but within ten minutes, I'm surrounded by a dense and steeply inclined rocky outcrop. When I spin around to check where I've come from, I find the rocks have crept up behind me and have closed in. *Oh dear...* The blood thumps in my belly. I try to leap and bound up the rocks to find higher ground, but it's like a goddamn dream: no matter where I climb, the territory is the same. I'm in a labyrinth and each higher rock reveals nothing more than another higher rock. I spring from one large boulder towards another but my legs have turned to jelly and so I slip. My right hand smashes into a rock, and my cheek catches the same rock on the way down. I'm crumpled between stone and spikey shrubs and blood is oozing from my hand and face. Fresh adrenaline pumps through my veins. The cuts are not deep but the frustration from allowing my skin to be broken forces out a yelping 'Fuck!' and then I let myself cry for two seconds.

Fucking great. I'm going to die out here on these rocks. Night will fall soon, and I'll freeze to death. And then the creepy crawlies will come out and feed on me. What an embarrassing way to die. Fucking goddammit! How did I let myself get into this stupid mess?

There's a rustling in the shrubs just ahead of me, and I lose myself to panic. An animal lurks in those bushes, I can sense it.

This is the end for me. This is how I die.

The sheep dog from the ruins below leaps out onto a rock and looks at me with her tongue hanging out. Sigh.

You've come to save me, haven't you?

The dog barks politely at me then turns and leaps off the rock. My breathing is heavy as I follow her, cautiously leaping from one boulder to the next down the hill. I stand still for a moment to catch my breath and rest my jelly legs. I spot the path descending from the Wind Gate.

A rush of relief. I'm not going to die today.

The sheep dog sniffs around Craig, asleep in the clearing and covered by evening shade. The uniformed man is gone. The dog licks Craig's face, and he springs up to a seated position.

'Nicko, you're back, mate. And you've made a friend,' he says scratching my saviour behind the ears. Craig yawns and stretches his arms and when I stagger towards him, he takes a closer look at me and says, 'Jesus! What happened to your face?'

'I nearly died,' I say. 'Let's get the fuck outta here.'

We trudge back into Ollantaytambo in the darkness of night. The sheep dog that saved me from the stone labyrinth followed us all the way to the bridge that crosses the river over into town, and at this point, she accepts a goodbye pat then trots off into a nearby farm.

I hug Craig and politely decline his invitation to go the pub. Before we part, we arrange to catch a taxi back to Cusco together tomorrow morning.

The lady at the front desk of my hotel cleans up my face and hand and applies bandages. In my bed, I lie uneasily under the covers. Despite my shattered body, the intensity of the day wires me awake.

Chapter Six
Return to Cusco

The Supertramp Hostel is fucked. My six-bed dorm room is dark, and it stinks of wet towels, packet-noodle farts and bad vibrations. The shared bathroom is small and dank, partially flooded and littered with toiletries. There's a locker at the foot of each bed and curtains hanging over the bunk. The beds are so small and closed in that I feel like I'm on a goddamn submarine.

After changing the bandages on my hand and cursing my rotten luck for a while, I pull myself out of my wooden coffin to make the trek into town. At a phone shop I make small talk with some gorgeous Israeli girls, and then kick myself because I didn't have the presence of mind nor bravado to exchange names, let alone take a number that I could text them on using my new Peruvian SIM Card. *Maldito idiota!*

At the Plaza de Armas, I notice for the first time the presence of the golden statue in the centre of the square. The dubious figure stands on a set of grey plastic steps that look like they've been dragged out of a community theatre production of *Cusco: The Musical*. Locals and tourists alike flock to the statue for selfies. I take a seat on one of the benches in the town square, insert my new SIM card and check my messages. Craig is staying way out on the edge of town. Cutting costs, he said. We arrange to meet up the day after tomorrow, to hang out for his last day in Cusco. I wrap my scarf a little tighter around my neck then cough and wheeze, struggling to draw breath in this thin, grimy air, then just sit and watch the world go by for a while.

*

Two days later I wake up suddenly to the crashing of church bells, having been kept up most of the night by the light outside my room and the pumping music of the nightclubs. I decided to check the fuck out of Supertramp Hostel yesterday and into a hotel room near the Plaza. I still back my decision despite the price increase and the rotten night's sleep. On the plus side, my wounds are healed and so it's with some gusto that I march out to the big golden statue in the Plaza de Armas to join Craig on a quest to explore Sacsayhuaman, the site that looks down upon the city of Cusco.

As Craig's decided to be on a tight budget today, we attempt to slip around the back of *Sexy-Woman*, as Craig calls it, to avoid paying the entrance fee. The sun is shining, and the air is warmer than it's been in days. It's beautiful, and yet there are hundreds of little monsters clawing at my mind from the inside. Taunting, picking, scratching, tormenting. *You're not having fun. You should go home. You miss your family. You've made a mistake. You are a failure. You are a pussy. Go and cry like a little bitch.*

Please, just fuck off!

It only adds to the downward spiral knowing that I *should* be having fun but I'm not. I'm supposed to be having the time of my life, but I am fucking miserable. Really, I just want to go home.

'You seem troubled, Nicko,' says Craig, tearing away half a mandarin and handing it to me.

I hesitate. 'I – it's, I'm just trying to figure out what I'm gonna do next month. That's all. I've got a couple of friends arriving in Cusco soon.'

'What's your plans?'

'We're gonna hike the Inca Trail, then fly to Iquitos. My mates have ten days booked at this ayahuasca centre, then they'll fly home. I'm booked in for two weeks. Then I'm thinking of getting a boat to Colombia and heading north from there.'

'Hey, these are good problems to have in life, bro. How long to stay in the jungle? How long to spend on Colombian beaches? This is living!'

I turn away and take a few deep breaths, then squat down on the bitumen. Craig sits down next to me. He gives me a light tap on the shoulder.

'It's alright to feel confused, mate,' he says. 'You can't expect to figure it all out straight away.'

My eyes are glossy and focussed on a little shrub one metre in front of me. 'I haven't really been coping that well,' I say. 'The reality of this trip is not matching up with my expectations. I've been in a pretty dark place the past week or so. I'm not sure whether I should keep travelling or bail back home.'

'It'll get better,' he says. 'You're still adjusting to life over here. Of-course it's gonna be a shock to the system. I was the same as you when I first got here. All fucked up in the head and crying about my misses every day. But it passed. You just gotta give yourself a chance to settle in.'

I nod my head and wipe the tears out of my eyes. 'Thanks, mate.' Craig helps me up and we continue our hike.

Sacsayhuaman is a breath-taking site. There are giant stones there that dwarf a human. If it were restored to its former glory, before the Spanish destroyed it to build their churches and their houses, the site would resemble a giant falcon. Of course, Craig and I don't get to see any of this because the staff don't let us in without a ticket.

After trudging back down the hill, we catch a local bus down to the neighbourhood Craig's staying in, some thirty minutes out of town. I'm not sure how he ended up in this neck of the woods. It seems Craig just packed his bags in Sydney and decided that he'd figure out all that pesky accommodation stuff when he arrived. In Ollantaytambo, he spent his first night sleeping on a park bench. Luckily, we met a pale-faced German girl at the pub, and she said she was going to look for a cheap hostel. She spoke excellent Spanish, so she was able to get them a good deal. I felt embarrassed about where I was staying, as my tiny private hotel room with the beautiful view was four times the price of their shared hostel room.

In Craig's neighbourhood we pick up some fruit from a corner store and take off for a hike to find some smaller scale, less touristy, and free, archaeological sites strewn across the hills at the edge of town. There are many winding paths leading through the forest, with old stone blocks worn away and hiding in the undergrowth. Local families enjoy picnics within the grass clearings. Little kids kick soccer balls or play hide-and-seek amongst the ancient Inca foundations. This is a place of effortless, inconspicuous magic.

In the fading light of the day, Craig and I attempt to hike to the top of a hill to catch a glimpse of Cusco from the highest point around. Two men in uniforms, reclining on a bank of grass, halt our progress. One is smoking a cigarette. The other fingers the gun on his waist. Both have moustaches. In broken English, they advise we turn around and go home. Something about farmers, guns, gringos, night-time and danger.

Craig waits with me at the bus stop.

'So this is it ay, champ?' he says.

'Enjoy yourself in Mexico,' I say.

'Cheers mate, looking forward to it. Stay in touch. It'd be great to have you up in Costa. Think about it, muchacho. And remember to fucken go easy on yourself.'

Craig hails down the bus for me. We hug and then I jump on.

The locals on the bus look at me like they've never seen a gringo before. I sit down by myself and space out watching the busy streets.

I have a feeling that everything is going to be alright.

Thirty minutes later, as I'm exiting the bus through the rear door, I accidentally bump a young man, and his plate of homemade baked goods falls to the ground. I apologise but the guy insists that it was his fault. I reach into my pocket and hand him ten soles, which is more than the value of the goods. He tries to turn down the money at first but eventually takes it.

'Thank you, my brother,' he says. 'Is so nice of you.'

And now we're friends. I know this because we do that whole tennis player handshake thing where your hand is diagonal, rather than horizontal. This handshake means not only are you friends, but both of you are as cool as professional tennis players. I ask my new amigo: '*Que direccion es Plaza de Armas?*' and he sends me on the right path.

And now my back is straight and tall, and my chest is puffed out and there's a smile on my face. In fact, each time I take a step, the universe softens the impact of my foot to the ground and then gently lifts it up again to propel me forward.

In my hotel room, I lie on the ground and play Karnivool's *Sound Awake* album. I visualise each part of my body softening and sinking into the floor. Then I spin over and do about twenty minutes of sun salutations. High on endorphins I decide to take myself out to Greens, a restaurant in the main square that washes its vegetables in filtered water. Just as I'm leaving my room, I catch a glimpse of my tattered copy of *Jitterbug Perfume* poking out of my daypack. I read the first page, close the book with a grin, and lay it down on my bedside table.

Outside the hotel, a drunken man attempts to steal a young woman's purse. He runs off down an alleyway when he sees me approaching. The girl is visibly shaken.

'Hey, are you alright?'

'Yes, I'm okay. That guy was a creep.' Latina accent. Probably not Peruvian though.

'I'm on my way to dinner in the Plaza. I can walk with you, if you'd like?'

'Ah, I'm okay,' she says. She looks scared and walks off on her own.

Adios señorita.

At Greens, I sit at the bar and order local beer, ceviche, a garden salad and a plate of par-boiled beets ("…the most intense of vegetables."). I savour every bite, making little satisfied sounds like some pompous food critic. I send Tinder messages to a few local girls and make conversation with two American ladies sitting next to me starting the Inca Trail hike tomorrow.

After dinner I stroll back towards my hotel and veer into the bar across the road towards the curious sounds of Jimi Hendrix riffs. I pull up a stool by myself and watch a local band play classic rock covers. After drinking two big bottles of beer and then a couple of Cuba Libres, I've got a nice buzz but for some goddamn reason, stumble into Chango, the dance club across the road. I hate it immediately but persist and chat up a Colombian girl. This fizzles into nothing pretty quickly and now reality has become rather fuzzy. I stumble out of the club and wander down the road into a burger joint. I manage to order a meal and make drunken friends with the dude sitting next to me. His name is Jesus. I tell Jesus that he's a legend and I thank him for dying for my sins. We make a cheers with our burgers, and I put my arm around his shoulder. Out on the street, a western girl asks if I have change for a one hundred sole note. She appears to be on drugs. I try to tell her to go away but when my mouth opens, only mumbles and jumbles of words come out, and she looks at me weirdly and asks for money again. A local girl appears at my side and starts stroking my arm.

'What does this bitch want?' asks the local girl.

Fucking hell. 'She's wants change for a blah blah blurphff…'

'I need change for a hundred sole note!' cries the western girl.

'You need to fuck off, gringo,' says the local girl. She softly takes hold of my arm with both hands. The local girl is about a foot shorter than me. She is not terribly attractive, but she has kind eyes.

'Where are you from?' she asks.

'Straya, burrrpff.'

'Where are you staying? Why don't you take me home, gringo?'

Are you a lady of the evening…? 'How much is for the night?'

'You think I am prostitute?'

'Well…' *Hmmm. Oops. Misread.*

'I'm no prostitute. I have boyfriend. But he cheat on me. So, I want to fuck gringo to get back at him. You want to fuck me?'

No, not really.

Well, kind of.

'Yeah okay,' I say. 'My hotel is just there.' I point to the building next door.

*

The following day I woke up feeling like a goddamn decrepit cave dwelling hobgoblin. In spite of this I still managed to drag myself out of bed to drop my dirty clothes off at a laundry service – I'm talking street level laundry service, so I'm basically a local at this stage – *and* I made the journey out to my Spanish lessons in the San Blas district. A few days later, though, my immune system finally gave up the fight against altitude, anxiety, dust, sleep deprivation and alcohol. And so now I'm lying in bed, surrounded by packets of cold and flu tablets and coughing and spluttering into a wad of soggy old tissues. I take out my phone and write a message to my friends Billy and Stan on our group chat.

Me: *Hey can you guys flick me an email with your return flight details. I'm considering coming home earlier than planned.*

Billy: *Haven't found a wife yet?*

Me: *Nah no wife. It'll be easier to explain later. I'm just tossing up whether to continue to Colombia by myself after you guys leave Iquitos, or whether I just bail home. Also, can one of you guys bring over some of that*

Betadine throat gargle? Stan, you know the one I'm talking about. Can't find it here.

Stan: *I've got ya sorted for Betadine. I'll also bring the last few episodes of* Game of Thrones *S6 so we can all watch them together and get startled like when The Red Woman turned out to be an old lady and frightened our boners away.*

*

The nightclubs in this area only pump their tunes on the weekends. The church seems to blast its bells every morning. These inconveniences, I can handle, but the one thing that's really starting to wear me down is the incessant fucking lamp outside my room, sending artificial, sleep cancelling light through each of the three goddamn windows of my hotel room. I asked a lady at the front desk if she could turn it off, but she told me that all the lights were on, 'for security reasons'. My bones are soft and sore, and my is head full of gunk. Just climbing out of bed is a chore, but I'm determined to have a decent sleep tonight, and so a little exertion now, to fix this problem, is necessary. I hang my travel towel and one of the hotel bath towels over the middle window and fasten them to the wooden frame with the physio tape I brought in case of ankle injury on the Inca Trail. A sacrificial blanket covers the right window, wrapped over the curtain frame, and when I manoeuvre the wardrobe a little bit it blocks most of the light coming through the left window. I admire my handiwork for a moment, then hack up a massive chunk of phlegm, scoot to the bathroom to spit it out, and finally creep back into bed. Finally. Darkness.

Just as I'm nodding off my phone pings.

Craig: *Nicko, you legend. I just got into Mexico. Sick place so far. Dead set best fish tacos I've ever eaten. Plenty of fine lookin' ladies around here too, mate, just saying. So, I was just thinking. Even if you decide to bail back to Aus early, we should at least catch up and travel together for a bit up here. The place is bloody beautiful, the weather's perfect, and I reckon you'd love it. It seems like we're in a similar head space at the moment, and I know this is starting to sound like a proposition... Essentially what I'm saying is let's at least grab a few beers on the beach and stare at pretty girls for a bit. What do ya say?*

Me: *Sounds good mate. You got a deal.*

Chapter Seven
Friends

When Billy arrives at the hotel lobby, I wrap him up in the tightest hug I can manage. Billy is tall and broadly built, with a beard and long black hair. He looks like what a man is supposed to look like. Billy owns guns, and he makes wooden tables as a hobby. He owns a house and a rental property. I met Billy in primary school, and we've played footy together since we were kids. Billy was always taller than the coach, even back then. He was six feet tall before he could spell. In high school, Billy used to smoke weed with me and Stan. We used to smoke in Billy's backyard on a Sunday afternoon when his parents were away, and we'd cook nachos and bake cookies and play indoor mini-cricket with a tiny little bat and ball.

Billy and I take a walk around town before strolling into the pub for breakfast beers and burgers. Billy is terribly jetlagged, having endured a long layover in Sydney. I'm hungover – from a regrettable night out drinking by myself – but the beers go down well. I ask Billy how the boys back home are doing, and he has little to report.

In the evening we walk to La Bodega 138, an Italian restaurant nestled up a hill on the way to the San Blas district.

'Where'd you find this place?' asks Billy.

'Trip Advisor. Found it on my tablet while you were having a nap.'

'Couldn't you just use your phone? I thought you'd be keen to leave as much technology behind as possible?'

'The tablet's handy for booking accommodation, flights, that kind of shit. Plus, I've got a little Bluetooth keyboard I use to write notes.'

'What kind of notes?'

'Like a travel journal.'

Billy takes a sip from his beer. 'Isn't a journal a bit queer, though?'

'What's wrong with being queer?'

'Journals are what fourteen-year-old girls write in. Do you start each day with, *Dear diary*?'

'Yeah man, I do. *Dear diary, Billy was mean to me today. He is such a dick.*'

We order more beer.

'Plus, whenever I've been travelling before,' I say, 'the thing that makes me the most anxious is the thought that my handwritten notebooks will be stolen. Like, if some bandits hold up my bus or rob me at knifepoint and steal my bag, then my notes'll be gone forever. Now I store typed notes in the cloud and take photos of my handwritten notes.'

'I read something about travel notes the other day,' says Billy. 'That if you take notes, then you just tend to remember those things, rather than all the other stuff from your trip. And we're better off just teaching our brain to remember everything.'

'I don't see it that way. When I read over my notes from a trip, just a few words can trigger a whole day that was seemingly lost.'

My phone pings with a message from a Swiss girl named Martina I've been chatting with on Tinder. I suggest we meet up for a drink at Paddy's Pub. She texts back to say she's with a friend for dinner but will meet Billy and me there afterwards.

Billy and I wait outside Paddy's in the cold. Martina approaches waving. We hug, and she gives me a kiss on the cheek. I say, 'It's a pleasure to meet you,' and we go inside. Martina is a cute little blonde-haired girl with rosy cheeks, big round glasses and soft pale skin. She drinks beer and is friendly and chatty and has this accent that is adorable, even bordering on comical. Mid-conversation, I place my hand on her leg and leave it resting on the fabric of her jeans. She lets her hand fall on top of mine and slowly strokes the skin on the back of my hand. We catch glances, and she smiles, and my heart beats fast.

The three of us wander into a salsa bar and order Pisco Sours. I swap spectacles with Martina, and we take cute photos. After five minutes of salsa on the dancefloor, I pull her close to me and we kiss.

*

The following days merge into one charming, effortless moment. Martina and I are both taking Spanish lessons in the mornings, though at different schools, and in the afternoons, Billy meets us in town and the three of us roam about the city taking in museums and historical sites. In the evenings, we meet with Martina's friends, watch soccer matches at the pub and drink beers and Pisco Sours. Martina and I make love in my hotel room, and somehow, Cusco doesn't seem like such a cold and lonely place anymore.

*

The façade of the Pariwana Hostel blends into an old colonial structure. Inside, there's a courtyard filled with bean bags, pool tables and young people. One of the girls from the front desk shows me and Billy upstairs to our triple-share room, next to a bathroom and toilet block. In our room there's a set of bunk-beds and one single floating bed. There's a small window with views of another colonial-era building. Billy claims the lower bunk, and I take the floating bed.

Stan arrives in the evening, and we drink in the hostel dining room.

'So how the fuck are you, boys?' asks Stan, as the three of us sit down at a long table with our cold beers. Stan is heavyset with a thick black beard. A tuft of black body hair pokes up out of the dip in his shirt. He wears his beer gut like a plate of furry, gaseous armour.

'Pretty good, mate,' says Billy, holding his beer aloft. 'Cheers, boys.'

We all clink our beers together and take a long chug.

'It's good to see you boys. Holy fuck,' says Stan, 'that flight over was a killer.'

'Likewise, mate,' I say. 'I'm glad to have both of you here with me.'

'You goin' alright, Nicko?' asks Stan. 'Seemed like you were struggling from your messages.'

'I'm feeling a lot better now. I was in a bit of a downward spiral.'

'Are you gonna come home with us then or stay on?' asks Stan.

'I'll stay on. I'm gonna hang with this bloke I met from Sydney after you guys take off from Iquitos. And then I guess I'll just play it by ear.'

Some young Europeans start singing karaoke and Stan joins them. We drink a few rounds of mojitos, but I feel sick and take myself to bed. Billy strides through the door soon after me, then coughs up a chunk of phlegm and goes to the bathroom to spit it out.

'That didn't sound so healthy,' I say.

'Got some kind of chest infection, I reckon.'

Stan crashes into the room and makes a general meal of launching his frame up the rails to the top bunk. 'Why the fuck am I on the top bunk, boys?'

'How'd it go with the Europeans?' asks Billy.

'I don't think they were really feeling my karaoke.'

I roll over to face the bunk beds. 'I was feeling it, mate.'

'Thanks bro.'

'Good night, fellas,' I say. 'I'm stoked you boys are here.'

A resounding fart blasts from the top bunk, quickly followed by a fart from the bottom bunk. Then a pause, and then another fart from the top bunk. I lean to the side and squeeze out my own fart and we can't help but laugh.

*

In the morning we bypass the free hostel cereal and take to the streets in search of something more substantial, settling on Museo del Café, a flash looking place tucked between the Plaza de Armas and the Centro de Convenciones. On the ground floor is the coffee museum that gives the place its name, and upstairs the café is immaculately set out with polished wooden floorboards and modern art on the walls. The waiters are sharply dressed and attentive. I order the vegetarian omelette, with pineapple juice and a long black. Billy and Stan both go for the full breakfast with fried eggs, bacon, sausage and tomatoes. When our waiter returns with our juice and our coffee, Stan asks for the WIFI password.

'What do you want the WIFI password for, dumb-dumb?' says Billy.

'Gotta see what's going on in the world, *brah*,' he replies, scrolling through his screen.

'We're in Cusco,' says Billy, 'why don't you put your fucken phone away.'

'What about my fantasy team?'

I chuckle.

'Mate,' says Billy, 'you're living in a fantasy *world*.'

Stan just shrugs his shoulders and scrolls away.

When we've eaten our breakfast and drunk our coffee and our juice, and each taken our turn to void our bowels in the *Museo* bathroom, we discuss plans.

'I thoroughly recommend Sacsayhuaman,' I say, having made a second trip after Craig and my failed attempt.

'*Sexy woman*?' asks Billy.

'Is that the one that Graham Hancock talks about?' asks Stan, one hand clutching his device. 'With the massive stones that all fit together perfectly?'

'Yep. It's that massive structure on the top of the hill overlooking Cusco, next to the big white *Christo*. I'll point it out when we go back to the Plaza de Armas. There's heaps of awesome archaeological sites around the Sacred Valley that we could do in a day trip.'

'Sounds good,' says Stan. 'I'm pretty much down for whatever.'

'First stop today, though,' says Billy, 'is *la farmacia*.'

I nod. 'How are *you* feeling, Stan?'

'Alright,' he says. 'Not a hundred percent. Dunno how much is altitude sickness and how much is hangover.'

'I haven't been a hundred percent since I got off the plane,' says Billy, before coughing up a chunk of phlegm, excusing himself and disappearing to the bathroom to flush it away.

On the way home from breakfast, we drop in to the chemist next to our hostel and back in the room we each take a cocktail of pain killers, cold and flu tablets, vitamins, multivitamins, antibiotics, probiotics and throat lozenges. My anxiety has dropped off to almost nothing but with all the beers and the Pisco Sours and whatnot, my health has deteriorated.

After a pharmacologically-induced afternoon nap, I duck over to the hostel bar and pick up a few cold beers. The three of us curl up onto Billy's bunk-bed and watch the second last episode of season six of *Game of Thrones*. Just as Ramsey is devoured by his own hounds, the power at the hostel cuts out, so we hit the streets and make for Norton's Pub.

*

While the accommodation is cheaper, and the vibe at Pariwana is certainly more vibrant than at the hotel, I've sacrificed a room of my own for a triple-share. This makes it more complicated to get alone time with Martina. She's living with a local family so rendezvousing at her place is not an option. One morning when Billy and Stan say they're keen to explore Sacsayhuaman, Martina and I take the opportunity to have the hostel room to ourselves. The man stationed at the Pariwana front desk reminds me that visitors to the hostel must remain on the ground floor.

'No going to your room,' he says.

'Of course,' I say nodding my head. 'No problem.'

And I lead Martina straight up the stairs to my room.

Martina rests her hand on my chest, her fingers wrapped up in the curls of my hair. Her head is nestled into my shoulder and her leg is draped over mine. I'm lying on my back with one arm wrapped around her body and the other resting behind my head.

'How did you meet Billy and Stan?' she asks, after a long, peaceful silence.

'We've been friends for ages. I met Billy in primary school, and Stan in high school.'

'That's nice you're still friends. I don't really keep in contact with many people from my school.'

'I've been living at Stan's place for a while now. We went travelling to the US together not so long ago. Back in 2014, I think it was. You know, it's weird. I just got this strange feeling that I'll probably never have as much fun as I did on that trip. I was old enough to travel with confidence, but young enough to want to party every day. It may well have been both the climax and the conclusion of my youth.'

'How does that make you feel?'

'Profound sadness and gratitude, both at the same time.'

We kiss for a while then Martina pulls away and says, 'We're not going to see each other again, are we?'

'We still have some time before I go. And we can hang out when I get back from Machu Picchu if you'd like.'

'And after that?'

'Seems unlikely.'

'If you're ever in Switzerland, send me a message.'

'I will. If you're ever in Australia…'

Profound sadness. Profound gratitude.

*

With only three sleeps until the Inca Trail, the little Nicky inside me is bursting with excitement. The boys and I picked up some cold weather gear and a few big bags of coca leaves from the San Pedro markets a few days ago, then did a day trip hiking to Rainbow Mountain. Stan struggled with the altitude; Billy and I fared easier, having had longer to acclimate.

That night we wander around the Plaza looking for a place to eat. Down a side alley near the Plaza de Armas a band of ruffians loitering on the street whisper 'weed, weed, cocaine, cocaine,' as we pass by.

'No *gracias*,' I say, holding up my hand. A police officer stands thirty metres away. Uninterested, oblivious, or perhaps part of a sinister trap.

There's little chance of us blending in with the locals. Stan's wearing a black singlet with an unbuttoned Hawaiian shirt over the top, cargo shorts and his hiking Merrels. Billy's wearing a polo shirt, hiking pants and his Merrels. I've tried to keep some sense of subtlety going with my brown suede shoes, black jeans and black t-shirt.

The restaurant spruikers come out like ghosts in a crypt.

'*Hola amigos!*' they say, thrusting menus. 'You want nice dinner, cheap drinks, free drinks.'

'Fuck all these guys,' says Billy. 'Let's go anywhere without someone peddling out the front.'

Eventually we choose one of the low-key chicken diners with no ghosts out the front. Inside, a gust of hot chicken air bursts out from the rotisserie grill behind the front counter. In the back courtyard there's a dozen or so Peruvian families spread out over plastic tables and chairs, with their chicken and chips and big bottles of Coca-Cola. Kids run around the courtyard playing with plastic toys while the adults watch the Spanish-language romantic drama on the television in the corner. It's a Peruvian *Bold and the Beautiful* equivalent, with the fuzzy picture and the dramatic looks and the sexy people. When we sit down, Stan asks for the WIFI password.

'No WIFI, sir,' says the waiter.

Billy rolls his eyes. 'It's a fucken chicken diner.'

'What?' says Stan.

I laugh.

We order two big bottles of beer and two big bottles of water. Stan and I each order half a chicken and chips. Billy is more controlled, ordering just a quarter.

'How are you guys feeling about going to the ayahuasca centre?' I ask.

'Not really sure,' says Billy. 'I'm not scared or anything, but like, not too excited. I'll just wait and see, I guess.'

'What about you, big guy?' I say, turning to Stan.

He makes a kind of frowny-face and bobs his head around. 'I'm not really sure either. I got a little insight into what the experience might be like from when I smoked some DMT over at Harry's place. I wouldn't really call that a breakthrough, though.'

'I don't know if I really want a breakthrough,' says Billy. 'From what Harry's told us, it sounds a bit fucked. Are you apprehensive at all, Nicko?'

'I am. But not in the sense of being scared of what might come up. I mean, I'm a bit scared of that. But I'm more afraid of something else.' I pause to sip my beer. 'My fear is that it's all just, kind of… bullshit. That this is all a big nothing.'

On the day before the trek, Martina and I check in to a nice hotel just off the Plaza de Armas. Somehow, the place is quiet, like an oasis in the heart of the city. After a warm shower, we make love and sleep until the late afternoon.

At night Billy, Stan and I meet the rest of our Inca Trail crew at the hotel next door to the Adventure Peru office. The lead guide, Carlos, is a larger-than-life character. He's tall, with Asiatic black hair, dark caramel skin, beer gut and a magnetic, confident swagger. His assistant Eddy is shorter and thinner than Carlos, and while he doesn't laugh like Carlos, he still wears a wry smile. It's like there's some inside joke that we don't know.

Carlos runs through a brief overview of the schedule for the hike. We'll be trekking for three days and three nights through the forests and mountains, following ancient Inca stone steps. On the fourth day we'll arrive at Machu Picchu.

'Okay chicos,' says Carlos, 'listen to me now.' He runs through the list of names on his list. He comes to us boys and laughs when he sees 'Australian' marked next to our names. 'Strahl - yans!' he says. 'Okay, we gonna have a good time.' He makes a drinking motion with this hand, then he laughs again, and his little eyes squint, and he grins like he's drunk.

'I think it's gonna be a good trek, boys,' says Stan.

Chapter Eight
The Inca Trail

The morning air is cold and biting, but I walk with purpose to the Adventure Peru office. Martina and I stayed up much of the night making love, and despite my lack of sleep, I am energised. Billy and Stan are already in the office with a few other early arrivals. Billy hands me a cup of steaming tea and introduces me to a middle-aged couple travelling from the US.

'We've left the kids with my sister,' says the woman. 'I don't wanna think about all the things they've already broken in her house. How are you guys doing with the altitude? I thought I was in good shape but I was puffed out just walking up the hill to get here.'

'Coca tea,' says Billy, and we raise our teacups.

The rain sprinkling and spitting against the windows of the bus made for a sombre ride but the frantic energy at the entrance to the trail breathes life into us sleepy gringos. Carlos and Eddy shepherd us to the ticket office, and we huddle under cover of the tin roof, rain pouring through the cracks. Around us, porters rush, filling enormous bags with pots and pans, sleeping bags, sacks of rice, vegetables, plastic containers full of raw meat, tent poles, tarpaulins and whatever else. All are young to middle-aged men, their faces hairless, smooth skinned and soft featured, except for the odd Romanesque nose. There are a few local women about as well, some draped in woven blankets, some carrying infants wrapped onto their backs.

There are delays at the entrance. Other tour groups gather. I look across to the bridge and the river gushing over the stones. My breath floats on the air. Then there is movement at the ticket office. Carlos waves for us to move across the bridge, and we're off. We cross the suspension bridge to the northern bank of the Rio Urubamba while the porters weigh-in.

We move eastward, with the river flowing to our right. Over on the southern side of the bank, the train-line follows the river through the valley, on its way to Machu Picchu. Up ahead, mountains rise to touch the clouds. We'll soon be leaving the river behind to head north over a mountain pass. The rain eases up as we stomp along the well-trodden path. The terrain feels surreal, like a movie set. Llamas and donkeys with rain-drenched faces pass by, led by men with leathery brown skin. Off the path, the vegetation is mostly tough woody plants and bushy shrubs, growing amongst the rocks. There are trees with beards, standing like old wizards. There are towering cacti with jagged thorns, and there are smaller, shrubby cacti with round disc-like flesh. A powerline cuts through the scene like a blooper on the movie set.

Carlos stops to explain some of the traditional uses of the plants around us. He's wearing a green-cream hat with the flap at the back. The kind of hat that teachers make you wear in primary school but if you had to wear it in high school, you'd fold the flap under to make it into a cap so the bullies wouldn't beat you up for being a nerd. Carlos leans with one hand on his walking pole; behind him Rio Urubamba rushes past, and over the river a small, ruined town crumbles around the train tracks. He nods and calls out to the porters as they lumber past, most with only sandals on their feet and each with large packs strapped to their backs. When the porters have overtaken, we press on along the path but before long Carlos gathers us together again atop a grassy hill and points down to a great ruined fortress below.

'This is the Pa-tall-aq-ta,' he says, 'or is also called Q'enti-marka. The name is mean *elevated place*, or, *the city on a platform*.'

The Rio Kusichaca provides a natural moat to the site, which is cut into the base of the mountain. The curved outer walls give the whole site the look of a great octopus with its tentacles cut at their base.

'This place was a religious site,' says Carlos. 'It was also used for the production of crops, and as a place for the soldiers to stay. Take some time here, take some photos, have a rest of your legs. We will keep walking in another fifteen minutes.'

Stan, with his camera poised, edges closer to a llama grazing in an open field. When the llama wanders away, Stan kneels to capture a photo of a lone, spiked and furry cactus, rising out of the rocky scrub with a single, bright red flower at its head.

Carlos calls for the gringos to press on, and we follow a trail to the northeast. Just off the path, I spot a fallen branch nestled into the low-lying vegetation and allow myself to be pulled into the scrub towards it. I clutch the branch in my right hand. The wood is smooth and thick, and it stands to my shoulder, with one end a bulbous head pointing skyward, and the other a clean slice resting atop the earth.

'Found yourself a wizard staff, mate?' says Billy, as I catch up with him and Stan.

'I didn't find the staff, brother, the staff found me.'

After a short day of hiking, we stop for the night in a small, grassed clearing. Carlos and Eddy help the porters construct a large dining tent, and the hiking crew intuitively separate into the men and the women, with the women congregating at the bathroom. The men stand around aimlessly by the tents until the middle-aged American man spots something and then disappears into a seemingly abandoned building. He calls out from behind a stone wall, 'Who wants beer?'

In the fading afternoon sun, the men enjoy a cool beer, with a light pattering of rain against our skin. After some manly banter, we join the others in the dining tent. Around the table now, there's a young couple from London, a long-limbed Swedish couple, the middle-aged American couple I first met at the hotel this morning, two young female high school teachers from France, and Rose, a soft-spoken American girl travelling by herself. The porters pass down bowls of steaming soup. Carlos thanks each man who pokes his head through the flaps of the dining tent. After we finish the soups, the porters pass in big plates of food to put in the middle of the table. There's a beef and vegetable stew, potato and tomato stew, fried rice with peas and corn, and piles of bread and butter.

Carlos sends around a shot of rum in our tea after dinner, which first lubricates the conversation but before long has everyone yawning and making moves to bed. The boys and I lie three abreast and fall asleep to the pattering of rain on our tent. It's been weeks since I've slept so goddamn well.

*

The terrain becomes even more lush on the second day as we press on to the north and follow the Rio Kusichaca through mystical forest. The porters stayed behind to clean and repack their bags before powering on again and they pass us gringos when we stop at a small outpost. A young girl smiles from within a simple mud brick structure. Her face is framed by a turquoise green painted windowsill, and she has a collection of bottled Gatorade, Coca-Cola and Inka Kola for sale. In a small dusty clearing, a lone chicken pecks around, and in a shaded spot a dog sleeps against a wooden pole. I kneel to inspect the dusty stone blocks of the path.

'Inca steps,' says Carlos, appearing next to me.

'These are the original stones?'

'Original stones of the Incas,' he says. 'Hey, Nich-o-lass. Strahl-yan. My man. You have some coca leaves for Carlos?'

I reach into my pocket and hand him my packet of leaves.

'Thank you, chico.'

The path shifts to the west and so begins an ascent through dense cloud forest along a tributary of the Kusichaka River. Beside us the stream flows gently over polished stone, occasionally hidden behind ferns and moss-covered trees. The flow of water is a kind of magical rushing white, and when I concentrate, I can feel the energy of the water pulsing through my wizard staff.

We break again at the base of a set of especially large Inca steps, with trees growing sporadically between the carved stone blocks and moss covering the ground along the sides of the path.

Rose looks distraught.

Stan wheezes and coughs. 'It's the altitude,' he says. 'I'm fucken struggling, boys.'

He grasps for his backpack zipper. I pass him a handful of coca leaves from my pocket. He stuffs a pile of leaves into his mouth then waves the packet to Rose. She shakes her head and whispers, 'No thanks.'

Carlos calls the gringos in closer to him. 'You may have noticed, my friends, that this Inca Trail is on a difficult path.' The gringos chuckle nervously. 'Maybe you ask Carlos why we take this path through the mountains when there is a much more easy path to take along the river. Is true, along the river is one easier path that follows the train tracks all the way to Machu Picchu. The reason we take this more difficult path is because this is the way of the Incas themselves.

'The kings, the priests, the nobles. They take this secret path through the mountains for security. You cannot bring armies this way. But more important, my friends, they is take this path through the mountains to be closer to the gods.' Carlos raises his long arms out to the mountains and the clouds and the sky. 'You see chicos, this is not *supposed* to be the easiest path. Machu Picchu is a sacred place, and the trail to the Machu Picchu, is a spiritual journey. For the Incas, this was a pilgrimage.

'Now,' he says with a wry smile, 'we will a start the hardest part of the trek. We will soon pass out of the forest, and then we will be climbing up the mountain. This is called the Warmi Wañuska. Is also known as the Dead Woman's Pass. When we reach the pass, I would like for you to wait for Carlos and for everyone, so we can take a break. Have a little snack. Take some sexy pictures all as a one group. And then we will walk to camp together.'

The Swedes plough on ahead, with Eddy endeavouring to keep up with them. Billy, Stan and I take off with the English couple and soon we have passed out of the cloud forest. The vegetation quickly becomes sparse, with trees and flowering bushes giving way to a modest covering of grass and shrubs. After forty or so minutes, Billy, Stan and I find ourselves separated from the herd. The English couple have plunged on ahead towards the Swedes and the rest are lagging, with Carlos to keep them encouraged and entertained. We take a break for water and coca.

'What do you reckon is the deal with the Swedes,' I say. 'Are they together?'

'Pretty sexy combo if they are,' says Billy.

'I was talking to one of the French chicks —' starts Stan.

'Were you now?' says Billy.

'—who said that the Swedes were just friends but have been travelling together for a few months. I think the Frenchies are single though.'

'What makes you say that?' asks Billy.

'We were chatting for a while and neither of them mentioned a boyfriend. And chicks usually go out of their way to bring up that they have a boyfriend around me. Chicks will cross the street just to tell me they have a boyfriend.'

We catch up with the English couple, and the French teachers catch up with us. Ahead, we can clearly see the peak. We pause to deliberate over where the Dead Woman's breasts and stomach and face might be. At the top of the pass, we nibble on muesli bars and bananas. Billy passes around his bag of coca leaves, and I pass around my lump of sweet brown activator that looks like a block of hash. I suck the moisture from the leaves down my throat as I roll together another wad.

It's a long wait. Especially for Rose.

'She didn't eat much for lunch,' says one of the French girls. 'And she refused to drink the coca tea at breakfast.'

'Why doesn't she drink it?' I ask.

'Because it's like, you know, used to make cocaine.'

'Is she worried about becoming addicted?'

'I don't know. She said she doesn't do drugs.'

'Weird,' says Stan, stuffing an enormous pile of leaves into his mouth.

*

On the third day, we reach the magnificent site of Phuyupatamarka. The structure bursts through the side of the mountain like a great spearhead, its stepped terraces reaching out towards the mist-soaked valley.

While the others clamber over the site, I sit alone on the grass of the lowest terrace with my wizard staff lying to my side, and look out into the valley below, cut by rivers and burgeoning with thick jungle. I close my eyes and feel the ground beneath me pulse, the stones behind me hum and the mountains around me boom. When I open my eyes, I perceive all of the sites along the Inca Trail connected like one giant Inca organism, and I realise that at one time, giant magicians walked the earth here.

After dinner, Carlos makes hot tea with rum again, and we all drift outside into the cold night to gaze up at the stars.

'Hey Nich-o-lass, do you have some coca leaves for Carlos?'

'Yeah sure,' I say, handing him my bag. He passes me the bottle of rum from his back pocket, before plunging an enormous handful of coca leaves into his mouth.

'Where is your home, chico?'

'I'm from Perth. It's on the other side of Australia from Sydney. I'm not sure if I want to move back there.'

'Are your family in Perth?' he asks.

'Most of them.'

'In Peru, we always live with our family. Is part of our culture. You guys, who is living in the West, is split up from your family. And when you get married and have babies, you make another new family. It's not like this in Peru. We stay with our family and make one big family. Everyone is more happy this way, together.'

'Where's your home, Carlos?'

'I am living in Cusco. I have my wife and a little baby as well. I am so proud. I have my parents and my wife's parents is close by as well.' Carlos takes a big breath then looks up to the stars. 'Hey, Strahl-yans! Where's the rest of the Strahl-yans?'

Billy and Stan and the rest of the crew come closer.

'Look up here at this one, this stars, chicos,' he says, pointing to a constellation. 'This one is very important for the Strahl-yans. Can anyone tell me which name is this one is?'

'That's the Southern Cross, mate,' says Billy.

'There she is, mate,' says Stan. 'Looking down on us.'

'That's right chicos, is the Southern Cross. Is very important for the Strahl-yans. But is very important for the Incas as well. Maybe you have seen the Chakana cross of the Incas? This Chakana cross is represent the Southern-Cross.'

Carlos flicks on his head torch and carves a symbol in the sand with a long stick. First, he draws a square, then cutting through the centre, draws an even-armed cross that completes the twelve-edged design. 'This is the Chakana. The symbol of the Incas. One, two, three, four points,' he says, tapping his stick at each of the flat outer points on the cross. 'The Inca Empire was divided into four regions, with Cusco, the capital, at the centre.' Carlos etches a small circle in the centre of the cross to represent Cusco. 'The Chakana mean many things for the Incas, chicos, and I'm not going to explain everything tonight. But I do want to talk about these steps.' He taps on the twelve edges of the repeated three-step design. 'These steps represent the three realms of the Incas and the spiritual animals that are the masters of these realms. The Condor is the spirit of the realm of the Sky. The Puma is the spirit of the realm here on the Earth. And the Snake is the spirit of the Underworld.'

Carlos' lesson reverberates in my mind, pushing out the boundaries a little. Looking up at the stars with my hot rum tea, I feel more relaxed than I have in a long time. The night sky is gorgeous, and I feel healthy and fit. Well, fitter, at least, than I've felt since I stumbled off the plane in Cusco. I have a soft buzz on from the rum and a glow of satisfaction from the trek. But something's still off inside me. I can't quite put my finger on it, but there's a tension that lingers like a splinter in my mind.

*

In the cold before first light, we pack our tents and bid farewell to the porters then grab our day packs and line up in the queue of gringos leading to the ticket gate. The boys and I yarn away sleepily as we chew our coca leaves and drink the last of our rum.

As the morning wears on, the forest begins to reveal itself, and the air becomes thick and hot. I push on ahead of the others, eager to reach the Sun Gate, but I become locked between clusters of American tourists. I overtake the Americans when they pause to high-five each other and take photos and sip from the water bags tucked inside their backpacks.

At last, my heart swells with excitement as I glimpse the final steps. I call out to some teen with a Spiderman backpack and say, 'Come on, mate, let's run up the stairs.' He just looks at me with disgust, so I fly up the stairs by myself and gasp for air as

I pass through the stone arches of the Sun Gate and look out upon Machu Picchu, nestled in the shade of vast and magnificent green mountains, with Wayna Picchu rising from behind and the Urubamba River slithering around in the valleys below.

It is more beautiful than I could ever have imagined.

Alone on a rock I sit and watch in silence until the sun rises over one set of the emerald peaks and bathes the site in golden light. There is a magnetic power in this place. I can feel it vibrating up from the stones. I understand what the Incas were doing here. Sweet, salty tears stream down my cheeks. This is awe. True awe. I understand now what I'm doing here in Peru. I feel it in my belly. I feel it well up in my throat. It pumps through my heart. I'm on a pilgrimage. This is a spiritual journey. Little blond Nicholas sits on his mother's chair in the study gazing at glossy images of sacred sites and now here I am. Living my childhood dream. I'm doing it. My heart bursts with golden light. This is too much for me to hold. I hide my face in my hands.

When the rest of the crew have caught up and we've all had a chance to rest and take photos, we descend the steps leading down to Machu Picchu. I cast my wizard staff off into the forest. *Thank you, my friend.*

There are some two hundred buildings spread over the site. Carlos points out the residential areas and the terraces used for agriculture. 'Machu Picchu,' he says, 'had many important historical artefacts, like pottery and sculptures, and very special jewellery. But chicos, many of these were taken by Hiram Bingham back to Yale University. In the one hundred years since the discovery of Machu Picchu, only thirty percent of the treasures have been returned to Peru. And these treasures were returned to *Lima*, chicos! Not to Cusco.'

Carlos explains what is known about the numerous temples and ceremonial areas, paying close attention to the Hitching Post of the Sun, the Temple of the Sun and The Room of the Three Windows. He speculates on what we might still discover on this site and buried in the jungles and forests around it. We pause at the submerged Chakana cross at the centre of the Temple of the Three Windows. 'Here you can see the upper half of the Chakana,' he says. 'The Incas design this way so that when the sun is shining, the lower half of the Chakana appears as a shadow on the ground. This shadow is representing the spirit realm.'

I wander around for hours with Billy and Stan, on a high, grinning and wide eyed like a kid in a theme park. In the late morning we climb up the stairs leading to the classic Machu Picchu postcard photo spot. From this vantage point I look down at the lost city of magic, cradled between great monuments of natural beauty. The green valleys. The winding alligator mountains. The sun-drenched site.

'We did it boys,' says Stan, and we bring it in for a three-way man-hug.

*

We may have had free rein of Machu Picchu in the morning, but by the early afternoon the tourists have begun to swarm, and tension is bubbling up from my belly into my chest. Young school groups pose for photos, looking as hot as possible; pursing their lips or flexing their arms or sticking out their butts and their tongues. Gaggles of ageing tourists dawdle, the men with enormous, phallic cameras swinging from their necks; the women in high heels and black jeans wielding selfie sticks like wands. Twanging, whiny parents bark orders at disinterested children, iPads grasped in their fat sausage hands. Families eat fried chicken picnics on grassed areas designated as no sitting zones. How long will it be, I wonder, before the Australians arrive in their boardshorts, singlets and bikinis, drinking beers and smoking darts? I turn to Billy and Stan and catch my deflated reflection in Billy's sunglasses.

'Let's get the fuck outta here,' I say.

So much for my spiritual journey.

The boys and I slump out across our seats on the train back to Ollantaytambo. Billy coughs up a chunk of phlegm, and Stan drifts swiftly to sleep. As I slip in and out of my own restless slumber, I catch glimpses of bizarre scenes. A man dressed as a demon bird squawks up and down the aisle. There's strange music as well, chaotic Peruvian flutes and drums. Wealthy American tourists clap along with the panpipe circus music, and they laugh and cheer. Considering the strength of these sinister vibrations, I wonder if I am in a goddamn nightmare.

What is this madness?

I close my eyes and pretend it's not happening.

At the end of the train ride, one of the wealthy American women comes up into my personal space and says, with a twinkle in her eye, 'Hey sleepy head, you missed out on a great show!'

I stare at her in silent disgust until she returns to her husband.

The Inca Trail is over. It was a beautiful experience. But it is most certainly over. Which means one thing: It's time to face the shadow again.

Tomorrow I'll be on a plane. And soon will start the next chapter.

Iquitos. The Jungle.

Ayahuasca.

The Unknown.

Part Two
Way of the Spirit
July 2016

Chapter Nine
Ayahuasca

Billy, Stan and I hover, sweating and apprehensive, in a large open dining room at Way of the Spirit Healing Centre. The room is encased by flywire walls, stretched from one wooden support beam to the next. In the centre of the room is a long wooden dining table, and against one of the flywire walls is a smaller table holding three big water drums and a stack of empty two-litre plastic bottles. Scattered across the floorboards under and around the smaller wooden table is a large pile of fresh green leaves. Deeper into the room is an open kitchen and a walkway leading to a set of stairs.

The young Peruvian man who met us at the riverbank on our arrival this afternoon gestures for us to take a seat at the dining table. 'Isabella is come, soon,' he says. 'Leave your bags here. We take them to your room.'

'No worries,' says Billy.

'*Hablas Español?*' he asks, twirling the little whispering hairs of his moustache with two fingers.

'*Un poco,*' I say shaking my head. 'Do you speak English?'

'No,' he says, smiling.

So, we sit in silence.

Earlier today we took a plane from Cusco to Lima, a plane from Lima to Iquitos, and a tut-tut-taxi from the Iquitos airport to an obscure and isolated nook of river, where a couple of old motorised canoes lay in the mud. The drive out from the airport revealed a grimy, bustling, smoggy jungle town smelling of car fumes, banana skins and street trash. Buildings hung by threads, with iron rods protruding and brick walls collapsing. Stray cats wandered about the streets with decomposing skin and infected eyes while vultures flew ominously overhead. At the river nook the banks were covered in so much rubbish that it seemed entirely possible the riverbank itself was just a pile of rubbish. It seemed preposterous to think we were in the right place, but there soon came a call from behind us. A fat man waddled out from his collapsing house and shuffled down the bank in our direction.

'Way of the Spirit?' I asked.

'*Si.*'

I turned to the boys and shrugged. We piled into one of the long wooden canoes, and the fat man manoeuvred the outboard motor and sent us down the river tributary. Naked children danced and splashed and bathed in the murky brown water. Some stood and waved and laughed at us. Older fishermen stared, stone-faced. Out on the water the jungle air was thick, and we were exposed to the relentless sun. Further down the river we cruised, and soon the buildings thinned from crumbling cement boxes to wooden huts on stilts. Finally, they disappeared completely, leaving only the trees to line the banks of the river.

When it was time, the fat man steered the canoe through a side stream and drove on until we slipped into a dark and shaded clearing and he found a place to bank our vessel.

'Oh-kay,' he said and held out his hand. Billy coughed up some coins, and we bustled off the canoe onto the muddy banks. The young Peruvian man with the whispering moustache was waiting for us there, slowly twirling his whiskers, and he beckoned for us to follow. And so now we're sitting at the dining table, silently waiting for something to happen...

A woman glides through the flywire doors to greet us, and I am taken by her beauty. She's tall and slender and moves gracefully in a flowing summer dress, her long brown hair cascading behind her. She looks like one of Tolkien's elven princesses, only with dark bronze skin.

'Hello guys, I'm Isabella,' she says, in a deep Italian accent. 'Welcome to Way of the Spirit, it is a pleasure to meet you.' Her cheekbones are high, her smile is wide, and her eyes are sharp and penetrating. 'Just so you know, Tony, the man who built this place, is away this week. He is in Romania speaking at a conference about plant medicines. He will be back in a few days. So, if you have any questions or issues, you can come to me.'

Isabella guides us along the thin wooden planks that lie across the middle of the grassed path cutting through the centre of Way of the Spirit. The walkway winds around and then passes through a wooden passageway surrounded either side by thick jungle. We follow closely until we reach the Maloka.

'This is where we conduct the ceremonies.'

The Maloka, a startling construction, is a vast circular room, with a dozen soft mats laid out around the perimeter. A star pentagram is carved into the polished wooden floorboards in the centre of the room. The ceiling is impossibly high, with a spider's web pattern built with the wooden beams at the pinnacle. Isabella shows us through a side door into a bathroom with three toilet cubicles, two showers, and a sink.

'Would you guys like to drink the medicine tonight?' asks Isabella, as we filter back out into the early afternoon sunshine. I tell her we haven't been eating a healthy diet these last few days, but she insists that won't be a problem.

'We were gonna just ease our way into things here,' says Stan. 'Maybe do a plant diet first?'

'It's probably better for you to start your work with the medicine straight away. Paulo, the ayahuascero, will do a reading for you in ceremony tonight with his wife Sandra, and that will give us a good idea about what kind of *dieta* you guys will need.'

'Alright,' I say, glancing towards the others. 'If you think it's best, then sign us up.'

I wonder if she can smell the Fear…

From ahead on the path, a slender black and white sheepdog approaches.

'Gaia has come to say hello,' says Isabella. The sheepdog lets us all stroke her coat. 'Gaia is the matriarch of this place.'

Gaia trots ahead, as Isabella guides us from the Maloka to our accommodation, Casa del Graham, named after one of the men who built Way of the Spirit with Tony some thirty years ago. It's a spacious, two-storey wooden house, with sunshine pouring in through the flywire walls. There are two beds downstairs, each enclosed in a mosquito net, along with a bookshelf, a rocking chair, two normal chairs and a writing desk. A curtain obscures one toilet, and a wooden door leads through to a bathroom with another toilet, a sink and a shower.

Our luggage is sitting in a pile by the front door. A millipede the size of my middle finger crawls out from under my bag.

'Okay, so settle in guys,' says Isabella. 'Make yourselves comfortable. If you need anything, I will be in a little office upstairs at the Big House, which is what we call the building where I met you. There's a great selection of books upstairs if you are interested, and some beanbags and hammocks. The ceremony tonight starts at seven. Just go straight to the Maloka when you are ready. It's probably best to arrive about fifteen minutes early to settle in.'

We thank Isabella and as the door swings shut behind her, Stan asks if we mind him taking the top floor. I offer Billy the slightly larger of the two beds downstairs, and reach down for my backpack, but leap back when a grey shadow stirs.

'What the fuck is that?' says Stan, backing away towards the stairs. A spider, the size of a gardening glove, stands poised with its front legs lifted like a boxer's fists. The spider advances, and I shuffle backwards. There's a flash of movement to my left as Billy launches a thong and catches the little beast flush.

'Jesus,' I say. 'What a shot.'

'Welcome to the jungle boys,' says Stan, ascending the stairs, but stopping sharply after a loud *crunch*. 'Shit boys,' he says. 'I just killed a millipede.'

Sheltered within my bed by the thick mosquito net and wearing my long, lightweight jungle pants and my long-sleeved checked shirt, with my stomach tied in a tight knot and my feet stretching out just beyond the limits of the mattress, my thoughts begin to run wild… *What if the medicine doesn't work? What if I'm a hopeless case, if nothing can help me? And what'll I do when Billy and Stan head back home? How will I go on my own this time?*

Will I crumble, like I did in Urubamba? And in Ollantaytambo... And in Cusco? Jesus. I think I've made a terrible mistake.

I close my eyes and try to concentrate on my breath.

*

Walled by shadows and trees we walk in the darkness to the Maloka, with just the three little circles of torch-light illuminating the path. The jungle smells of fresh bark and decomposing leaves, and the shrill of insects vibrates in the air. A piercing hoot cuts through the insects like a poison dart and into my mind, and a wave of understanding and excitement charges through me...

Holy shit, Nicholas, just think about what's going on here! You're in Iquitos. In the Peruvian Amazon. In an ayahuasca centre. Walking the path to a ceremony!

I shake my head, as if trying to cast out the old, silly thoughts, and chuckle to myself. The knot in my stomach unfolds, and I walk with renewed anticipation.

There are half a dozen people lying on mats when we enter the Maloka. Luckily, we manage to find places next to each other close to the entrance. In the centre of the room, a large pot billows smoke from atop the wooden pentagram, and around it sits softly flickering candles. On one side of the room is the door to the bathrooms. On the other side of the room is a table adorned with ornaments and bottles of liquid and softly glowing candles. There's a shadowed couple lying on a large mat next to the table. I assume this is Paulo and Sandra, the ayahuasceros. Next to them, sits Isabella, and beside her is a round, bald man, a kind of Buddha-like figure. I take my socks off and lay them next to my water bottle. There's a bucket near my pillow and a blanket on the end of my mat.

Isabella comes to sit by the three of us newcomers. 'Did you settle in okay, guys?' We nod and smile, and she offers us some mapacho, holding out a handful of pre-rolled cigarettes of different sizes. Some are slender, like the kind beautiful French women smoke, and some are thick, like the kind Cuban dictators smoke. 'This is pure tobacco from the jungle,' she says. 'We use this in ceremony. Sometimes you can use them to bring on the medicine, if perhaps after a second cup, you still don't feel like the medicine is taking effect. We also use the mapacho sometimes if the medicine is too intense, and we want to ground ourselves. It works either way, you just set your intention.'

We each accept a few of the slender mapacho cigarettes.

Paulo, the ayahuascero, rises from his mat and selects a dark bottle from the table then walks over to the young man lying to my left, who promptly slides up to the end of his mat and slurps down a spoonful of whatever Paulo has in his bottle. The ayahuascero cleans the spoon with a cloth then rises and moves towards me. I scoot to the top of my mat and sit crossed-legged.

'*Como estas*?' asks the ayahuascero.

'*Bien*,' I reply. '*Es nombre Paulo*?'

'*Si*,' he says. '*Hablas Español*?'

'Ahh. No, not really. *Solo un poco.*'

'Oh-kay,' says Paulo, and he pours a spoonful of his black medicine into a silver spoon and holds it out before me. I slurp the liquid and thank him. The taste is bittersweet and earthy. It's not ayahuasca, but it tastes similar. Paulo moves on to Billy, and then to Stan and when he's made it around the whole Maloka, he returns the dark bottle to the table and walks over to the pot in the centre of the room. He places a lid on the pot to kill the smoke then picks it up and carries it over to the wooden table. He returns to his mat next to Sandra and starts to hum. I lie down and close my eyes.

Sometime later, Isabella calls out the name *Sam*. I shift my head and peer through slits as the young guy to my left takes a seat on the floor in front of Isabella, Paulo and Sandra. I can't hear their discussion, but it ends with the young guy taking a drink from a cup and then returning to his mat. The blood pulses in my gut.

Inhale.

Exhale.

'Nicholas.'

Here we go…

Candlelight flickers across the solemn faces of Isabella and the ayahuasceros.

'How are you feeling?' asks Isabella.

'Nervous.'

'That's normal.'

Paulo pours the brew into a small brown cup then hands it to me. I hold the cup to my lips and almost wretch with the smell.

Please, let me have a good night.

I pour the liquid into my mouth. The brew is thick and bitter, and tastes of vile and concentrated earth and yeast and dirt. I swallow and breath out deeply, then bring my hands together in-front of my chest in a gesture of prayer and say thank you to Isabella and the ayahuasceros. I rise and return to my mat.

It is done.

My mouth still holds the aftertaste, so I sip some water to try to flush it away. I light a mapacho and inhale and only just manage to suppress a violent cough before the tobacco smoke sends my brain swirling. Another sip of water, a softer drag from the mapacho, and then I sit and watch as my friends drink the medicine. When everyone has drunk, Isabella rises from her seat to blow out the candles in the centre of the room, and the Maloka is plunged into darkness.

Without warning, Paulo begins to sing. His voice is deep and haunting. Subtle and soft yet powerful. Now Sandra harmonises with lighter notes. These are the *icaros*, the medicine songs. I listen, I wait and I breathe, and before long, have reached a state of relative calm.

Isabella's voice slices through the silence. 'Would anyone like a second cup?'

A shadow shifts from across the Maloka and sits by her and the ayahuasceros. The shadow moves back to its mat. Two other shadows from across the room follow. I rise from my mat and walk over to take a second cup. When I've returned to my mat, Paulo sings to settle us all down again and then begins the shamanic readings. Sam, the guy to my left, is first. Then Isabella and the ayahuasceros appear at my mat. They waft smoke with a fan of feathers and sing to me, a haunting, rhythmic chant. Isabella sways with their music. 'Close your eyes,' she says, and a spray of alcohol hits my face. Paulo sucks the air around me and blows the alcohol again. He leans towards Isabella and mutters to her in Spanish.

'Paulo says there is a blockage in your mind. And a blockage in your abdomen. It's like a piece of phlegm is stuck there, energetically speaking.'

'Okay,' I whisper.

'Paulo recommends starting a tobacco diet tomorrow. Have a good night, Nicholas.'

I thank Isabella and bow to Paulo and Sandra, and then they move on to Billy. I lie back down on my mat.

What the fuck does that mean?

Time slides by. I close my eyes, try not to think, and before long find myself immersed in a slow meandering walk through hypnogogia.

*

Paulo finishes a particularly beautiful and melancholy *icaro* and then begins to speak in Spanish. I can't understand exactly what he says, but I register something like, *comer un plátano*. A few people call out 'thank you' so I assume this means we're at the end of the ceremony. Isabella rises from her mat and lights the candles in the centre of the room. A strong vibration passes through my body. Glancing up to the ceiling, now illuminated by candlelight, I notice the interlocking spiderweb pattern is spinning and folding into itself.

Well, that's *a little disconcerting.*

The people around me begin to move about the room and talk with each other. Isabella appears next to me. 'How was your night?' she asks, perhaps for the first time, but I'm not sure. Feeling rather confused I take a banana from her and try to communicate.

'It came on late,' I mumble, the words taking an age to fall out of my mouth. 'I'm… still feeling… something.'

A complex fractal overlay has pasted itself across my perceptual field.

'Just take it easy,' she says. 'You can take all the time you need.'

I lie back down and spoon my pillow. My eyes are watering, and something's jamming open my mouth. My belly is swollen and the air around me is thick and heavy. I notice I'm rocking back and forth but can't settle down. Something feels wrong. I can make out Billy and Stan, sitting up and chatting softly to each other, but feel terribly distant from them. I notice myself mumbling nonsense into my pillow. Drool slides from the sides of my lips onto the pillow.

Something's definitely wrong.

I've become enveloped by a strange and sinking feeling of dread.

I can't breathe. I can't breathe. I can't breathe!

'Should we go back to *Casa del Butt*?' calls Stan from somewhere. Billy says something as well, but I don't register.

'I just need…' I mumble in reply. 'I just need… another minute, dudes.'

A sharp pain in my stomach! And an urgent rushing of saliva to my mouth. I haul myself up into a leaning position, just hovering over my bucket. My brain spins and tumbles the blood pounds in my temples like rising drums.

And then it comes…

A black, moving grid is transposed over my bucket as I purge. A bizarre moment of grinding, sloshing, buzzing as the sickness bellows out of me and splashes into the bottom of the bucket. Out the liquid pours as I heave over and over and over. One final heave and I drain the last of the vomit into my bucket and lie back down onto my mat, shaken, but relieved, and almost instantly, I feel like my normal self again.

*

As I brush my teeth in the bathroom at Casa del Graham, scanning the room for creepy crawlies, a ghastly sound rings out from deep in the jungle.

'*Wagh!*' it goes, like some kind of jungle demon.

'What the fuck was *that?*' calls Stan, who's sitting on the rocking chair in the living room. I rush out to join the boys.

'*Wagh!*' comes another chilling cry.

'Jesus,' says Stan. 'Imagine being a little Indigenous kid out here in the jungle back in the day with one of those fucken ghouls crying out in the night.'

'The horror,' says Billy.

A crunch.

'Ah, shit boys,' says Stan, 'I just destroyed another millipede. Poor bastard crawled under the rocking chair and chopped itself in half.'

Before bed I slither into the bathroom and notice for the first time the piece of laminated paper stuck to the wall. I shine my torchlight over the words. I don't recognise the writer and there's no reference below. I read the note a few times through, not knowing quite what to make of it...

'It is possible to get out of a trap. However, in order to break out of a prison, one first must confess to being in a prison. The trap is man's emotional structure, his character structure. There is little use in devising systems of thought about the nature of the trap if the only thing to do in order to get out of the trap is to know the trap and to find the exit. Everything else is utterly useless...

...All this is, seen from outside the trap, incomprehensible to a simple mind. It is even somehow insane. Why don't they see and move toward the clearly visible exit? As soon as they get close to the exit, they start screaming and run away from it. As soon as anyone among them tries to get out, they kill him. Only a very few slip out of the trap in the dark night when everybody is asleep.'

Chapter Ten
Tobacco

Paulo arrives early in the morning with three tall glasses of light brown liquid. He's wearing long pants, and an old black singlet covers his thick, wiry torso.

'*Hola Paulo*,' I say. '*Qué es?*'

'Tobacco,' he says, with soft eyes and a wide grin.

We assemble before him. Stan drinks his glass in one long gulp. Billy finishes his soon after. The tea smells of stale water and smoke and burns my throat all the way down. It takes me seven big gulps to drink the spicy, ashy liquid.

'Oh-kay,' says Paulo, when I hand him my finished glass. '*Bien*.' He bids us good day and leaves with the empty glasses.

The morning sun seems to flood into the house now with added intensity. My pores become flush with sweat, and my mouth fills with saliva. Stan vomits his tobacco up into a bucket.

Isabella strides through our front door to find the three of us with pained expressions on our faces. Billy and I are sitting cross-legged on the floor. Stan is draped onto the rocking chair, his head floating sheepishly above his heavy bucket. After checking in with how we all are, Isabella tells us that we will have another cup of tobacco at about four in the afternoon. 'Then your last drink will be tomorrow morning,' she says. 'It's best if you do not touch the skin of other people in this time as you will be very open, energetically. There will be an ayahuasca ceremony tomorrow night, which you are welcome to attend. Often the tobacco *dieta* helps to make a strong connection to the medicine.' She explains that workers will bring us our meals and advises we remain here in Casa del Graham, to stay with our 'process'. The morning after the ayahuasca ceremony, the *dieta* will be cut by Esmerelda, the chef, and then we will be free to join the others in the Big House for breakfast.

When Isabella glides out the front door, Billy slips away to the bathroom to raucously spew out his tobacco.

'You know what that tobacco tastes like?' says Stan.

'Horror,' calls Billy from the bathroom.

'Yeah,' continues Stan. 'And like, a glass of ciggie butts that's been left outside in the rain after a party.'

Later in the morning, a sprightly local girl brings in two large jugs of green smoothie. The boys and I drag together three chairs and sit in the living room. The tobacco is still inside me, so I hold off drinking my breakfast.

'So,' I say, as my mates each chug from a glass of thick green liquid. 'What do you guys make of your first experiences with aya?'

Billy just shrugs and takes another drink from his smoothie. 'Nothing much, really,' he says. 'Felt sick most of the night. Had a massive spew at the end.'

'My night was pretty interesting,' says Stan. 'I spent a lot of time exploring the landscapes from *Destiny* –'

Billy laughs. 'The game?'

'Yeah.'

'It is your *destiny* to be a fucken nerd,' says Billy.

'It was awesome, dude. I was flying over The Vault of Glass. Venus was all terraformed. It was dope. But then I had this profound realisation about myself. I used to be proud of like, being big and strong. It was a key part of my identity, you know, being a "big guy". But now that I've let myself become a fat bastard, I don't feel I've got the same status in the world. I guess I've been pretending I don't care that I'm not as physically strong anymore, but I do. Anyway, it all came up last night while I was lying in the foetal position and feeling super sad.'

Billy and Stan drink from their smoothies. I brush a millipede away from my foot. A tree branch crashes to the jungle floor.

'And then there was this guiding presence,' says Stan, 'and I realised the happiest times in my life have been when I've had a state of equilibrium, balancing all the important things in my life like family, relationships, work, making music, chilling with the boys, playing sport. Those are the times when I've been happiest. When I got injured playing rugby that threw everything out of balance. I stopped exercising, started eating shit, played video games all the time, and basically just lost sight of the bigger picture.'

'Balance, hey,' I say.

'Fucken equilibrium, boys,' says Stan.

'What about you Nicko?' asks Billy. 'Any insights?'

'Not really. I didn't have a strong visionary experience like you did, Stan. But I did have a massive purge at the end.'

'That sounded *powerful!*' says Stan.

'It was. The aya took ages to kick in for me. It wasn't until the end of the ceremony that I started feeling it.'

'And you had two cups, ay?' says Billy.

'Yeah. Hopefully, this tobacco diet will help get things moving.' My stomach rumbles as if on cue. I feel the tobacco working inside my body. I'm not sure exactly what it's doing in there, but I can feel it doing *some*thing. 'Hey boys, I feel a little light-headed,' I say. Billy and Stan nod, and then we all laugh. I collapse to the floor cackling.

A band of grey furred monkeys, the size of small dogs, circle the house as we sit in the living room waiting for our breakfast to digest. Billy imitates their call. 'Hoot, hoot, hoot!'

'I think they're replying to you,' I say.

'How's the wall of sound out here?' says Stan.

Billy imitates the monkeys again.

'Especially at night,' I say.

'Beats the city,' says Billy.

I think of Cusco and the nightclubs and the church bells and the traffic and the fucking firecrackers. I think of the Inca Trail and the sounds of rain, gently pitter-pattering onto our tent or the gentle, calming flow of the river.

Billy falls asleep on the hammock, Stan moves upstairs to read, and I shift onto the rocking chair. Aside from stomach cramps and jittery limbs, I feel relaxed. It's a strange feeling to have arrived at this centre and to be immediately isolated from everyone else. But I'm comfortable in this house, and I'm grateful for that. There's a desk I can use to work on my writing. There are two toilets and plenty of spare buckets. The toilets themselves are just a bucket covered by a wooden frame and plastic seat, with tub of sawdust next to it. There's a spare bed upstairs we can use as a day bed.

Standing alone on the wooden desk is my breakfast smoothie, still untouched.

'Not yet,' I mumble.

And predictably, my thoughts turn to memories of food…

My Dad's side of the family is Greek, and on most Sunday evenings, there'd be at least a dozen of us around the dinner table at my papou and yiayia's house devouring vast plates of food. Fuck. I can taste it now. Cabbage leaves stuffed with rice and minced meat. Salads with cucumber, tomato, onion and olives, doused in olive oil and lemon juice, sprinkled with dried oregano and topped with slabs of feta cheese. Layers of baked pita filled with sweet pumpkin, or leek and feta cheese. Roast legs of lamb or pork, with crisp skin and gooey fat. Potato casseroles in light tomato sauce, with chicken legs and thighs. And lemon and egg white soup, either on its own, or with chicken legs, or with meatballs made from lamb and veal, parsley and garlic. Or sometimes Yiayia would dust the meatballs with flour and fry them in oil and serve them on their own. And she par-boiled broccoli and cauliflower, and soaked them in olive oil and lemon juice and salt. And she always laid out crusty bread and feta cheese and olives and marinated chillies. My papou would have his own jar of marinated chillies next to him where he sat, proudly at the head of the table…

Fuck it! I could be waiting the rest of my life before I purge this goddamn tobacco!

I wolf down my breakfast smoothie and gently swing on the hammock, flicking through my old worn-out copy of *Jitterbug Perfume*.

In a late passage, Robbins describes humankind's evolution beyond reptilian and mammalian consciousness into *floral* consciousness. This seems rather appropriate considering I'm currently coalescing with multiple plant consciousnesses. In the following passage, Robbins argues that the most intense spiritual experiences involve, in some way, the suspension of time.

'It is the feeling of being outside of time,' he writes, 'of being timeless, that is the source of ecstasy in meditation, chanting, hypnosis, and psychedelic drug experiences. Although it is briefer and less lucid, a timeless, egoless state (the ego exists in time, not space) is achieved in sexual orgasm, which is precisely why orgasm feels so good. Even drunks, in their crude, inadequate way, are searching for the timeless time. Alcoholism is an imperfect spiritual longing.'

A fleeting flash of existence outside of time.

Le petite morte.

Finally, in the early afternoon, I spew up my tobacco. It's not a psychedelic experience like an ayahuasca purge, it's just a regular old spew into a bucket.

About thirty minutes later, Paulo arrives with the second cup, and my heart sinks. I swill this one down faster than the first. Billy and Stan are quick to throw theirs up, but again, my tobacco stays down.

When the girls arrive in the early evening with bowls of porridge and fresh bananas and jugs of coconut water, I still haven't purged, but am overcome by hunger. We light candles and arrange them around the living room. The temperature has dropped, and the noise of the insects has picked up. A few mosquitos make it in through the protective fly-wire shield. Mosquitos have a short life. Once they hatch, they search for a blood-meal to get the nutrients they need to breed. And then that's it for them. The call of the insects at night is a call to feed and to fuck. And they either reproduce then die. Or they don't reproduce then die.

'Do you think you'll see Martina again?' asks Billy, before taking a mouthful of porridge.

'Doubt it,' I reply. 'She was lovely. But I can't see a scenario when we'd meet again. I'm not making plans to go to Switzerland, and she's not making plans to come to Australia. But you know, spending time with her got me feeling like I'm ready for a committed relationship again.'

Yeah, right mate, so you can fuck that one up as well. Great plan.

'Sick of banging Tinder chicks?' says Stan.

'Something like that.'

'Yeah, must be tough,' says Billy. 'So, how's it going with *your* missus, Stan?'

'It's alright,' he replies. 'I'm a bit concerned though. I didn't realise we wouldn't have WIFI here. I forgot to call her to say that we were leaving Cusco.'

'You didn't realise that we wouldn't have WIFI?' asks Billy.

'Yeah.'

'In the jungle?'

'It's cool. I'll send her a text if we go on a trip into town.'

*

Three young women come to our house in the morning to clean. A young toddler dances around the house in a little summer dress with a soft doll in her arms. The women sweep the floors, make the beds and replace the buckets of shit and vomit. They take away the bowls and jugs from dinner the night before, then smile and leave.

And then Paulo comes with our fucking tobacco.

I try to explain that I haven't spewed any of the tobacco yet. '*No purga el tobacco*,' I say to Paulo. I use my hands to gesture vomit coming out of my mouth and then shake my head.

Behind me, Stan downs his glass and almost immediately throws it back up again into a bucket. I nod to Paulo, point to Stan, and say, '*Stan es purga. Para me, no es purga.*'

Paulo nods.

'*Por qué no es purga?*' I ask.

Paulo grins. '*Esta noche,*' he says. '*Esta noche, es la ceremonia.*'

'Okay Paulo, *muchos gracias.*'

Paulo departs.

Billy hears something and runs upstairs. 'Boys! Come up here,' he says.

Stan and I run upstairs to find our mate crouched down by the flywire wall, talking to a tiny red monkey. Another dozen primitive primates launch themselves from the branches of nearby trees and onto the balcony. These little red monkeys have whiskers that look like little moustaches, and must be half the size of the grey species that circle the house each morning and afternoon. The closest monkey screeches and scratches against the fly wire, then leaps away to join the rest of the family on the wooden balustrades. Billy slips his head out of the balcony door and tosses an old banana peel towards the monkeys, then retreats into the house as they swarm upon it.

*

Most of the mats are already taken when we enter the Maloka. The boys and I find ourselves in a similar position to the first ceremony. The round, bald Buddha-like man is in the same place. Paulo's wife is not in ceremony tonight, and Tony, the man who built this place, is still away. I take a mat next to Sam again, and he gives me a little nod as I sit down. The door is immediately to my right. Billy takes the mat across the door space, and Stan takes the mat to the right of Billy. It's silly, I know, but I feel physically disconnected from my friends.

Isabella rises from her mat and blows out the candles in the centre of the room. I count ten strangers around the room.

Deep breaths Nicko…

Inhale.

Exhale.

I decided earlier today to ask for a big cup. The first ceremony was alright for an introduction but I need to know that this whole thing is the real deal. I'm not sure what it'll feel like or look like but I need some kind of sign.

My stomach gurgles. I still haven't purged since the first glass of tobacco.

Sam is the first to be called. I am the second. I sit cross-legged in front of Paulo and Isabella. Paulo pours my cup.

'*Es posible por más?*'

'*Más?*' he says, with a raised eyebrow.

'*Si, por favor.*'

Paulo nods and obliges. I pour the brew into my mouth and swallow. I cringe, gather my breath, then bring my hands together in prayer, thank Isabella and Paulo, and take my seat. I light a mapacho and watch as the others get up to take their medicine.

When it's time, I rise to take a second cup.

'I'm not feeling the medicine.'

Paulo nods and fills the cup right to the top.

'Ahh, okay,' starts Isabella. 'That is a big cup, Nicholas. Please, do not feel that you have to drink all of that. Just take what you are comfortable with. You can leave some in the cup, it's okay.'

It takes me three mouthfuls and all my strength, but I take it all down.

'Gracias.'

Jesus. That was heavy.

I light a mapacho and smoke half of it, and then lie down on my back. Sam is into the experience early; I notice him swaying with Paulo's songs. I close my eyes and return to my breath. Strange sensations permeate my body, a kind of light tingling, sinking feeling. By concentrating, I can bring on some light visual patterns, but I have to really focus or else they disappear.

If I can just focus all my energy on

– Fuck! This isn't the real thing! I'm just pretending…

I guess ayahuasca just doesn't work for me.

I curl up onto my side and try to get some sleep.

*

There is commotion in the Maloka. First there was moaning. Now yelling. A voice calls out from a mat close to the bathroom.

'Hey Isabella,' comes an English accent. 'He's gone and locked 'imself in the toilet again.'

Isabella leaps up from her mat and disappears into the darkness of the bathroom.

I close my eyes.

When I open them, Isabella is crossing the Maloka from the bathroom and back to her mat. Soon after, Paulo rises to begin the shamanic readings, and Isabella joins him. Sam is not on his mat, so Paulo comes to me first. After my icaro, Paulo sprays the alcohol onto my face and body. Isabella translates. 'Good connection,' she says. 'Enjoy your night.'

Good connection? I can't feel anything.

… But when Paulo sits down on his mat after the shamanic readings, I *do* feel something. There's a kind of stoned heaviness to my body, like I'm being pressed down into the mat.

Paulo quickly stands up again and shuffles across the Maloka and into the bathroom. The faint sounds of his icaro floats out into the Maloka

…and that's when I hear it…

Oh, my fuck.

It's the *Language!*

Thrall! Thromping, thandros, thanatos!

The words catapult, and they boomerang, and they fire, and they whiplash.

Thromping!

Thrahhghning!

Thraalllll!

And then, *Boom!* The flash! And I enter an alien palace of bright, technicoloured terror. A world of interweaving, tumbling, melting fractals. I know this place. This is the DMT Realm. It's incredibly bright and colourful and oozing and folding. It's sparkling yellow, green and purple. It's bejewelled, and it is molten. It entices and it horrifies. All of life is mundane in comparison to this. Nothing has ever been more immediate. Agony and ecstasy in a single moment. In one sense *so* familiar, and in another, *so* shocking and astonishing and horrifying, and just when the fuck does it end! It's too much to take! I can't breathe anymore.

Oh God. *The Fear!*

It seems to take an age but eventually I fall out of the DMT Realm and can once again perceive the world immediately around me. Only I've carried with me a sense of impending disaster. Paulo is talking, way off in the distance. I curl into a ball. Tossing, turning, driving down into the mat. Something has gone wrong. Something has happened to me. Voices ring out around the room. Someone lights the candles.

Oh, fuck no. It cannot be.

The ceremony is over…

I open my eyes a slither and see bodies moving about the room, gathering together, giggling and talking. I drive my face down into my pillow. This is too much. It's too intense. I want it to be over but the medicine only grows more powerful, overwhelming my body. The people crawl around the room like monkeys, communicating with each other in strange little mouth noises that I can't understand. Oh God, the Fear! *The Fear! The fear that the whole universe is a projection of my own mind. But if this is all my creation, then might all this just be a dream? Might I have dreamt this whole thing? Not just this experience in the Maloka right now, but my whole life? Fuck. What if I have dreamt my whole life? I'm going to wake up soon and realise everything I think is real, everything I think has happened in my life, has just been an elaborate dream. This is going to happen. I know this. I'm going to wake up soon and see my true life, for the first time. I'm scared. I'm so fucking scared. Make it stop.*

I open my eyes to the sheer chaos in the room. The monkeys are crawling about, itching and scratching and squeaking with each other. Hugging, touching, laughing.

But I am alone. I'm not welcome here. I'm not part of the tribe. I'm the outsider.

I close my eyes again and drive my head into the pillow. My mouth is locked open, silently leaking saliva.

I need help.

I crawl over to Stan and Billy and collapse between them. I try to speak, but only nonsense comes out of my mouth. They are talking to me, but I can't understand them. They are monkeys as well. I wriggle around like a man possessed. This won't do. I crawl back to my mat. I fumble with my water bottle, eventually opening it to take a sip.

Wait. Did I just crawl over to the boys?

Or did I imagine it?

Maybe I astral projected over there?

How many times have I crawled over there?

I look down at my mat.

This is a magic carpet. I can teleport.

Don't you see what this means? It means you are a wizard.

Wizard!

Isabella appears next to me.

'Hello, Nicholas. Are you in the medicine?' she asks.

'Yes…very…much,' I say, aware of how slowly the words are falling out of my mouth.

'Okay,' she says, smiling. 'Just let me know if you need anything.'

I remember the moaning from the bathroom.

Oh no.

A terrible sinking feeling envelops me.

Was that me *in the bathroom? Have* I *been the one yelling and moaning? Have I been disrupting everyone's night? Oh God. Is it me? Am I the fool? Everyone will laugh at me. I'm going to wake up naked in the middle of the room, aren't I? I am the outsider. I am the fool.*

I fold the pillow over my head and rock myself like a child, mouth ajar and tears streaming down my face.

I am the fool. I am the fool. I am the fool!

…Until a dark shadow winds its way from the central wooden spiderweb of the Maloka down into my chest and splits me open from the inside and my body dissolves…

…And.

Time.

And.

Form.
Slip.
Away.
Into.
Meaninglessness…

*

Where is the rest of me? I wonder, now that I'm no longer with my body, floating on some plane I cannot explain.

No space and no time. This is what Tom Robbins was writing about.

That's funny, I remember Tom Robbins, and yet have no idea what I am.

I notice laughter.

Oh, so I have form again?

No. Just laughter. Still no form.

What am I then?

There is no *me*.

There is no *I*.

What *is* there then?

What do I do when there's nothing to hold on to?

And what if this madness goes on forever? Oh shit, this is forever! This is Eternity! Oh no, The Fear again! I'm going mad! That's what's happening here. Madness! Madness for Eternity! There is no end! The Horror!

*

There is a voice.

The voice has come to soothe me.

All things are impermanent, my brother. Just breathe and this too shall pass.

Inhale.

Exhale.

*

I peer through the slits of my eyes. The bucket is in front of my face. I sense I am curled on my mat. It feels like there is a pillow under my head. Water leaks out of my eyes and my lips. My feet are warm. I open my eyes a little more. Gaia, the black and white sheepdog is lying at my feet. I am protected. I close my eyes.

*

Sam is with me. He touches my shoulder and then he touches my leg and then he sits on the end of my mat, facing the centre of the Maloka. He sways back and forth, as though there is an energy force moving through him.

'Oh, fuck yeah,' he says. 'Fuck yeah!'

I writhe around on the mat, driving my head into the pillow. My body is shaking, contorting, vibrating, moving of its own accord. I open my eyes and prop myself up onto one shoulder, saliva falls from my mouth. Sam turns to face me.

Can he see The Fear?

'Nicholas, brother. Come on over here,' he says. 'Come over to your friends.'

I crawl beside Sam, across the chasm of the Maloka, to Stan and Billy, and lie between them.

Remember to breathe, Nick.

I cannot speak to my friends, but I know that I am safe. Now, I can relax.

… *No, I can't! I must purge!*

I scramble back to my mat and grasp my bucket.

All time has been building up to this moment. This is the single most significant moment in all of space-time. There is an almighty heave into the bucket. An enormous volume of liquid gushes from my body. The entire universe around me collapses and refuckulates itself back to the reality I am more familiar with.

Another purge!

And another!

Five or six great, frothy voluminous heaves and then I collapse, my body on the mat, my face on the wooden floor of the Maloka, gasping for air.

Cheers ring out from around the room.

I smile and close my eyes.

When I've gathered enough strength, I push my bucket to the side and lift myself up to a cross-legged seating position with my back against the wall. I close my eyes and the background chitter-chatter of the monkey-people melts away, and I enter an endless moment of perfect meditation. Around me, the world is light green and yellow liquid fractals. My body has evaporated again but this time, I have retained my sense of self and it is heavenly. Blissful. This is it. I've reached the centre. I have reached the core. I have reached perfect unity.

*

I open my eyes and grasp my water bottle. I drink a mouthful, feeling wonderful. A shirtless figure slithers over to Sam, who is now sitting on his mat.

'Are you ready for our chat?' asks the figure.

'I've never been more ready in my life,' replies Sam. I chuckle and decide to crawl back over to Stan and Billy.

I lie down between my friends, and my heart explodes.

This moment eclipses all previous experience. This moment is gushing euphoria! This is the Joy of Being! The pure Joy of Being! I suck in air through my nose and push it out of my mouth like I'm breathing for the first time. I've never felt so real in my life. I've never been so alive in my life. I gasp the air into my body like it is a drug. I am intoxicated on oxygen and life. I feel an endless rush. This is the greatest high in the world. Wave after wave after wave of Joy. So much Joy I cannot contain it all and it begins to hurt and so I cry. I am grateful for everything and everyone in the world. I've never known such gratitude. I roll around the floor laughing and breathing. There has been nothing more real before this. This is life. This simply, *is*.

I have no more doubt. I have broken through.

I laugh and turn to Billy. 'Transcendence,' is all I manage to say.

The night sky opens, and rain falls on the jungle.

Chapter Eleven
San Pedro

Billy, Stan and I leave Casa del Graham behind us and wander along the wooden steps towards the Big House for breakfast. The jungle encroaches on either side of the path, and below, thousands of ants ferry leaves and other insects and whatever-else along. On further, we come to a clearing in the jungle where there's mud and grass rather than thick vegetation on either side of the wooden planks. Two dogs tear around a corner barking and chasing a fleeing group of chickens. Under the cover of trees, a group of Peruvian men gather around a large, steaming cast-iron pot. I give them the old chin nod. A couple of the men notice and give me a head nod in reply.

Out the front of the Big House is a pile of thongs and shoes. Inside, Isabella sits at the dining table in a loose floral dress. She looks magnificent. There are two guys in singlets sitting on the far side of the breakfast table behind tall green smoothies. I recognise Sam. He's clean-shaven and lean and looks a couple of years younger than me. The second guy, a skinny English bloke, introduces himself as Jasper. I recognise him now as the bloke that crawled over to Sam last night to ask if he was 'ready for their chat'.

I thank Sam for helping me last night.

'That's my pleasure, brother,' he says in a soft Canadian accent. 'It was a big night for me as well.'

'Too right you had a big night, Sam,' says Jasper, 'You only went and locked yourself in the bloody toilets again.'

'At least I kept my clothes on this time.'

'That's something I guess,' says Jasper. 'Now that we're on the topic, can I ask if it was cubicle number one?'

'Might've been.'

'I'm telling you, mate, that cubicle is cursed. If ever something goes down in the bathroom, it goes down in cubicle number one. The number of times I've bloody locked myself in that toilet and spent the whole ceremony in the dark depths of the unconscious. It's a scary place, fellas,' he says, turning to face me and the boys. 'Believe me, I know.'

'The cubicle is not cursed,' says Isabella, before exhaling a cloud of mapacho smoke, as though it were an exclamation point.

'Where's everyone else?' asks Billy. 'Seemed like there were more people in the ceremony last night.'

'Many are on diet right now,' says Isabella. 'Some are on a tobacco diet, some on another plant diet. I think some people are just deciding to sleep in this morning, after last night. Now guys, before you get too settled, it's time for Esmerelda to cut your tobacco diet.'

Right on cue, a robust woman in jeans and a t-shirt, as tall as Billy and almost as wide as Stan, emerges from the kitchen with a big smile on her face and a plate of chilli, salt and lime in her hand. Esmerelda says something in Spanish, then gestures for me and the boys to follow her through the hallway, past the stairs, and out into a courtyard. She wafts Palo Santo smoke around us all then demonstrates what to do. We take some chilli and salt and crunch it around in our mouths for a while, then chew on a chunk of lime and spit the whole masticated mush out onto the jungle floor. Esmerelda cheers, then lays a big old hug onto each of us.

'*Huevos?*' she asks.

'*Sí!*'

When we've finished eating our eggs, Stan asks if he can have one of Isabella's mapachos.

'Sure,' she says, tossing him her pouch. 'I can buy some for you in town, if you like? I will probably go in today.'

'Yes please,' says Stan. Isabella turns to me and Billy and we both nod.

'Okay, I will buy for everyone,' she says. 'Just for your information guys, we hold ayahuasca ceremonies on Monday, Wednesday, Friday and Saturday nights. There is no obligation, but if you would like to sit, then put your name down on the whiteboard next to the kitchen. Also, we will be holding a kambo ceremony tomorrow.'

'What's that?' asks Billy.

Jasper, the skinny English bloke, laughs.

'Kambo is another sacred medicine,' says Isabella. 'It is poison taken from a specific kind of frog in the jungle. We burn the skin, and then put on the medicine. It works like a kind of vaccination to boost the immune system.'

'What's it feel like?' asks Stan.

'Fucking horrible,' says Jasper. 'You feel like you might be dying. Like, it's proper poison, right. And you purge, like with every other bloody plant in this place.'

'For some of the tribes in the jungle,' says Isabella, 'the ayahuasca, the tobacco and the kambo are all sacred and vital to their practice. They use all three as part of an integrated system of medicine. It's alright if you don't want to sign up for the ceremony tomorrow, we hold one almost every week, depending on how many people are interested. You can also do a coca ceremony with Charlie the coca shaman. He has been sitting in ceremony lately, holding space while Tony has been away.'

Charlie must be the round Buddha-like fellow.

'What about San Pedro?' asks Stan. 'How do we sign up for that?'

'If the three of you are interested in San Pedro, you could probably do that tomorrow instead of kambo?'

Stan turns to me and Billy, and we each nod in approval.

Upstairs at the Big House there's a hammock and a pile of bean bags. On one side of the room is a large bookshelf and a flywire door to a room with a bed. On the other side is a door to an open office with a computer, desk and a set of drawers. Billy slings himself out on the hammock, and Stan and I each take a beanbag.

'So, Nicko,' says Stan. 'What the fuck happened to you last night?'

'That was a big one,' I say, lighting one of Isabella's mapachos. 'Last night was like nothing I've ever experienced before in my life. It was everything I hoped for, and yet in no way was I prepared. It took ages for it to come on, like in the first ceremony. I thought it was all over and I was in for a quiet night. But then I heard the *Language*. And that's when I knew that something was gonna happen.'

'The *Language*?' says Billy.

'It's the same language I heard when I smoked DMT out the back of Stan's place. Terence McKenna describes something similar, like, the sounds are strangely familiar, but they don't make any sense. Syntax without meaning or something like that. And then it was like *boom!* And I was in a DMT flash. I really don't know how to describe it. It's like, in the flash I'm blasted out into another world or realm, and there's the classic fractals all around. It all moves and pulses, and it all feels very alien.' I take another drag from my mapacho. 'But at the same time, it kinda feels familiar as well. Like I'm home. I dunno.'

'What was going on when you were crawling around on the floor?' asks Stan.

'I was meaning to ask you guys about that. I wasn't sure if I crawled over to you guys, or if I just imagined it.'

'You definitely came over to hang with us a couple times,' says Billy.

'I suppose there were two major stages that I was going back and forth from. There was this *realm*, where everything was fully alien, and I'd left my body, and my whole sense of self as well. And then there's the other experience where I'm in my body and I'm myself, and I'm in the room, but I'm freaking out.

'There was this one time when I was experiencing the Maloka as if it was a little nook in a tree and we were all little marsupials or primates or something, and everyone was talking. I felt like a toddler wandering about the family home with strange and scary adults laughing and screeching. You know? Just movement and colours and chaos. Strange beings all around making strange noises. All of it alien and frightening. I imagine that's what it's like sometimes as a kid. There's all the adults around and they're speaking, and you know they're saying things, but you don't understand them, and you try to express yourself, but they can't understand you. You think they're all playing a trick on you.'

*

Morning sunshine pours through the open fly wire walls upstairs in Casa del Graham where Isabella, slender and graceful, wafts sage smoke around the room while Billy, Stan and I sit patiently waiting for our San Pedro. After cleansing the space, Isabella sits on the floor next to us and burns some Palo Santo wood, then she spoons four tablespoons of powdered green cactus into each of the three bowls in front of her.

'Fill your bowl with water,' she says, 'and stir quickly. Try to get the medicine down as fast as you can. If you leave it too long, then the San Pedro can turn to sludge, which is not very pleasant.'

I pour enough water to cover the green powder then stir and take my first gulp.

Ugh.

Wet chalk.

The second gulp is more terrible than the first. Billy's bowl is almost finished. Stan's too. I look down at my bowl and frown. With my hesitation, the powder has turned into gloopy sludge.

'How did you guys get that down so fast?'

'You need more water, bro,' says Stan, before letting out a shattering belch. I add more water, basically filling the bowl up again, and look down in disbelief. It's like I'm starting all over again. But the mixture is looser this time and eventually, I take it all down.

'Okay guys, good work,' says Isabella. 'I'll leave you to your process now. Someone will come with bowls of fruit for your lunch in the afternoon. If you would like to go for another dose in a couple of hours, then you can find me in the Big House. Feel free to come to dinner at the regular time. We will have mouth orgasm for dessert tonight, as a treat for you guys who are drinking San Pedro today.'

'What's a mouth orgasm?' asks Billy.

'It's delicious,' says Isabella. 'I think it's better to leave it as a surprise.'

Isabella leaves, and I shift to lie on my back on the floor, flicking a millipede away.

Stan says, 'I think Isabella is going to orgasm in our mouths tonight while we are on drugs.'

'Stop it,' I say.

*

I clutch my stomach and gently rock myself in the hammock. I feel nauseated and stoned. The boys and I oscillated between conversation and personal reflection for a couple of hours but Stan's upstairs reading now, and Billy's just slipped into bed. I close my eyes and watch my thoughts turn to my family…

On my mother's side, the blood is English and Irish, with lines reaching back to the colonial oppressors, convicts, outcasts and well-intentioned settlers that destroyed the way of life of the Australian Aboriginal peoples that had walked the land for sixty thousand years. On my father's side, the blood is Greek, and those roots were pulled from a small village outside Thessaloniki after the Second World War.

Relations are not great with my maternal grandfather. We don't have much to do with him these days, not since my grandmother died. He and my grandma used to drink a lot, according to Mum. Then Grandma had a stroke. I don't know how old she was when it happened but my only memories of her are in a wheelchair, with slurred speech and a wonky right arm. I remember her tapping away at her typewriter with her bumbling left hand, 'writing her stories', as she used to say, with her right-hand spastic and tucked up by her shoulder. Despite her broken body, she seemed forever to be in good spirits, and was always excited to see me.

My grandfather, who stayed with her through her slow decline into death, was seldom in good spirits. He used to yell at Grandma, exasperated. It must have been sweet relief for them both when she eventually left this world. He didn't cry at her funeral. Men of that generation don't cry. And Grandpa was certainly a man of his generation. He still drinks as much as ever. His belly is enormous. It's one of those classic old man beer bellies. He's got standard issue legs and arms – he still plays golf and tennis, even though he's walking on artificial hips and knees – but then planted on this regular frame is a bulbous keg of sixty years of fermenting beer. Whether I like it or not, I'm a part of him just as he is a part of me. I notice I've been adopting one of his mannerisms: clutching my hands over the top of my belly. I must have lost weight already. I can feel a bone right at the base of my sternum that I never knew existed.

My paternal grandfather, my papou, died a few years back. He and my yiayia met while they were still living in the village back in northern Greece. The story goes that my papou came to my yiayia's house and asked for her hand in marriage. My yiayia didn't want to at first, so she ran away. But my papou persisted, and I guess one day his cheeky smile worked its magic on her. After World War II had destroyed their village, my papou and yiayia moved to Australia together to start a new life, along with my papou's three brothers. My papou and his brothers built four identical houses in a row in an outer northern suburb of Perth. The houses are still there today. My papou died in his garden, and my yiayia still mourns him. We're not sure exactly in what order it happened, but my papou fell off his ladder, had a stroke and collapsed in the backyard. I still remember his face as he lay unconscious in a hospital bed. I remember the tubes in his mouth and the machine pumping his chest. The family decided to increase the pain medication so he could drift away. My papou loved his garden. It's where he was most at home. There was no more appropriate place for the old man to spend his final conscious moments.

*

It's dinner time and I'm still feeling this cactus. Gravity is particularly difficult to manage. We've left the safety of Casa del Graham to venture out to the Big House. The boys and I toss off our shoes outside and take a seat at the table. I smile to the faces, unable to articulate words. I sit next to Isabella and catch a glimpse of her exposed breast as she leans forward to take some salad. My goodness she is beautiful. It almost hurts.

The dinner table is glowing with candlelight when Esmerelda, the chef, brings out a big silver bowl full of gooey chocolate caramel.

'Okay guys,' says Isabella, passing around some silver spoons, 'as you took the San Pedro today, you can have first serves of the mouth orgasm.'

'This is delightful,' says Billy licking his spoon, while Stan makes a kind of strange humming sound through his wide smile and glazed eyes.

I take a spoonful of the chocolate goo and let it slide down my throat. I still can't talk so I just nod and smile until my head sinks down and rests upon the dining table.

'What's in it?' asks Billy.

'Oh, there is raw cacao,' says Isabella, 'some cinnamon, coconut oil, a few other things as well.' Isabella checks her watch. 'Do you hear a boat?'

Stan shrugs. I blink a few times and mumble into the table. From this vantage point I make out the whiteboard hanging by the kitchen. As well as the ayahuasca and kambo sign-up spaces, there's a little space that reads: *Coca Ceremony with Charlie.*

Hmmm… I have some questions for that man…

'I think Tony has arrived,' says Isabella. 'I'm going to go see. Are you guys okay to blow out the candles when you leave?'

'Should be able to manage,' says Billy.

For some reason I feel uneasy about meeting Tony, the mysterious figure who built this place. It's like we've been hanging out in his house while he's been away and we're about to get busted. Before we leave for Casa del Graham, Billy, Stan and I sign up for the ayahuasca ceremony on Monday night, and I put my name down on the whiteboard for a coca ceremony with Charlie.

Chapter Twelve
Visions, Fear & Poison

The rain came down this morning, and with it some respite from the draining jungle heat. I'm still shitting out volumes of green San Pedro sludge, but I've regained my powers of movement and speech. There are a couple of new faces sitting at the breakfast table in the Big House. Tony, the big guy himself, is standing by the passageway to the kitchen. I recognise him from photos on the website. Tony is tall and clean shaven, with a strong jaw and a strong build. He's wearing long white linen pants and a loose-fitting button-up shirt. He looks more like a retired football player than a medicine-man. The boys and I introduce ourselves.

'How have you settled in?' asks Tony. His Great Lakes accent is deep and clean.

'It's been great so far,' I say.

'Excellent. I'll make time to sit down with each of you to talk about your intentions. But not today. This morning, I have to give these dietas.' He takes two jugs from one of the kitchen staff. 'Are you guys going to be in ceremony tonight?'

'We're all signed up,' says Stan.

'Great. I'll do a reading on each of you, and we'll go from there. See you tonight.'

After breakfast, the boys and I float upstairs. Stan and Billy each select a book, and I smoke a mapacho in a hammock and consider what happens when I leave this place. I've made tentative plans to get on a boat from Iquitos to Leticia, the border-town on the southern-most point of Colombia, where the country meets Peru and Brazil on the Amazon River. The alternative is to catch a plane from Iquitos to Lima and then to Colombia, but the idea of cruising down the Amazon on a boat feels romantic and exciting. I imagine relaxing on an open deck, smoking mapachos amongst strange and eccentric characters, gazing out into the thick forest, monkeys swinging through the trees and old fishing boats rocking on the water.

*

I'm lurching back and forth on the rocking chair at Casa del Graham with an empty bucket between my legs feeling terrible and wishing that the purge would just come already. I reached the end of this, my third ayahuasca ceremony at Way of the Spirit, without vomiting and without the Language or the DMT Realm or monkeys squeaking strange mouth noises or transcendence. To be honest, after the intensity of the second ceremony, it was a relief to get out of the Maloka with my sanity intact. Tony performed a shamanic reading on me and said there were blockages in my body and in my mind. 'You're not allowing yourself to feel,' he said. I'm not so sure what he meant. *How exactly do I stop myself from feeling something?* I shuffle away to the bathroom and take matters into my own hands by sticking my fingers down my throat. I sit naked on the toilet just in case. Soon, the purge hurls out of my mouth and cannons into the base of the bucket. When it's all out of me, I wash my hands and face and settle back into the rocking chair, much lighter and fresher.

'You really get that good spew going, don't you?' says Stan.

'It's impressive,' adds Billy. 'In terms of sheer volume and the strength of the spew going into the bucket.'

I nod. 'It's such a relief when it comes.'

'That's one of the interesting things I've found,' says Stan. 'The spew is actually not such a bad thing. I know a lot of people are put off by the idea of vomiting when they hear about ayahuasca.'

'We've probably got more experience spewing than most,' says Billy. 'You know 'cos we've played like a million games of Circle of Death.'

I glance down at the bucket, having carried it with me out of the bathroom. 'I might just go release this into the wild.'

Outside, the moon is full and bright. My vision is greatly enhanced and penetrates through the layers of trees. After tossing the spew onto some shrub and setting the bucket down, I wander along the wooden path, allowing the jungle to pull me in. My skin is light blue and alive and tingling pleasantly all over my body. The forest seems to pulse back and forth, as though it were breathing. *I guess I'm not out of the medicine after all…*

Something in the jungle screeches and I scurry back inside.

Billy and Stan are still sitting in the living room.

'How'd you guys go tonight?' I ask.

'I spewed after about twenty minutes,' says Billy, 'and that was about it.'

'It was a pretty mild night for me as well,' I say.

'The aya came on after about ten minutes for me,' says Stan. *Must be nice…*

'And pretty soon,' says Stan, 'the Maloka was glowing fluorescent green and violet. I was surrounded by peacock feather patterns. Paulo was in the middle of the Maloka, but he was wearing a flaming headdress. And then I had this overwhelming sense of *belonging* with all the other people here. It was like we were all one giant organism, experiencing consciousness both individually and simultaneously. I heard someone clear their throat, and it felt like *I* had cleared my throat. I heard someone purge, it felt like *I* had purged.'

'That might have been me,' says Billy.

'Then I felt this tremendous need to shit,' says Stan. 'And I freaked out 'cos I thought I'd already done it in my pants. I hadn't by the way, I went and checked after. But then I remember this soothing voice and a hand stroking me. It was saying: *It's okay baby, I've got you.* I thought it might have been Isabella—'

Oh God, I wish…

'—but it was a vision. And that was when I realised that my relationship with my mum has fallen apart. I thought about it and couldn't even remember why I've had so much anger towards her. When I sobered up, all I could think about was getting home and giving her a big hug and telling her that I love her, and that I'm sorry for being a bad son.'

Billy puts his hand on Stan's shoulder. 'That's beautiful, mate,' he says, and I agree.

'I love you dudes,' says Stan.

'I love you dudes too,' I say.

A high-pitched birdcall pulls us away from the heartfelt moment.

'You hear that bird?' asks Billy. 'Don't you reckon it sounds like it's saying, *oh wow!*'

Stan and I chuckle and listen closely.

133

'*Oh wow!*' comes a cry from the jungle.

'It's like it's super surprised by everything,' says Stan.

'Like a puppy crossed with a goldfish,' says Billy. 'Every moment is new, and everything is exciting.'

'*Oh wow!*'

We wait in silent anticipation…

'*Wagh!*'

'The ghoul!' cries Stan.

In bed, the medicine teases me and keeps me from sleep.

*

It's late morning and I'm sitting cross-legged in a small room facing Charlie, the round, bald, Buddha-like man. He's wearing a long white robe, and his bald head is damp with sweat. He has soft eyes and an unassuming smile. Perched in the side of his mouth is one of those big old bommyknocker mapachos. Between us, a large pile of coca leaves rests atop a square of coloured fabric. Around the piece of fabric, Charlie has arranged a series of ceremonial items: stones, beads, cards, various green and white powders, little figures and symbols. Next to him sits a hand-crafted drum.

I must admit that I'm sceptical about this ceremony. I don't see how I can achieve any kind of breakthrough without the aid of strong, psychedelic drugs. Nonetheless, this *is* an opportunity to talk about my experiences so far at Way of the Spirit and get some advice from this man who is clearly something of an institution here.

Charlie blows mapacho smoke around the both of us and over the coca leaves. He blows smoke into his hands and pushes the smoke over his face like he's bathing at a river's edge.

'This is a safe space,' he says, in an East–London accent. 'Here, we are bound by Sacred Lore. You're free to share anything here, and I will never repeat it. You may choose to repeat what happens here, but I can't.'

I nod.

He chews.

'Do you have a relationship with coca?' he asks.

'I used it a lot when I was in Cusco, mostly to manage altitude sickness, and to help when I was hiking in the Sacred Valley.'

'So, you've met coca, that's good. Have you used coca in ceremony?'

'Never.'

Charlie shows me how to take a few leaves and roll into a parcel. We add a white powder as an activator, working in a similar way to the hashish-like blocks I used on the Inca Trail. He instructs me to carefully select another small handful of coca leaves and watches closely as I make my choices. I place the second parcel into my mouth and jam it next to the first with my tongue. While we chew, I tell Charlie about my path to Way of the Spirit and my experiences with ayahuasca, especially the breakthrough in my second ceremony.

'By the end of it,' I tell him, 'I was overwhelmed with a profound sense of relief and gratitude just to be alive. I'd never felt so alive before in my life. It was like I was breathing air for the first time. It felt mystical. I don't know how else to describe it.'

Charlie nods and carries on chewing. I feel like I could tell this man anything and he'd just carry on nodding and chewing.

I babble away to Charlie about my troubles with work and women and where to live and well, the general mess that is my life. When I mention that I'm trying to become a writer he says that will help with my 'integration', then he places a deck of cards face down in front of me.

'Take these cards,' he says. 'Shuffle them until you form a connection with them, then choose two.'

The backs of the cards are bright blue with a yellow lightning bolt down the centre. I take the deck in my hands and shuffle, then fan the cards out in front of me and select two.

The Vision Quest.

The Frog.

'Hmm,' I mutter. 'I've been discussing doing kambo with my friends.'

Charlie smiles. 'Then today we'll do a vision quest to find your power animal.'

I lie down on a mattress pressed up against one side of the room. In my mind, and following Charlie's directions, I walk to a colossal tree with a door in its trunk. I open the door and speak these words:

I will pass down to the world below and find my power animal.

An impenetrable wall of trees extends out to my left and to my right. Rabbits scurry about in the undergrowth, amongst soft shrubs and flowering bushes. A white wolf appears ahead of me. The wolf changes into a horse, and we ride together along a path through the woods. The horse grows wings, and we fly through blue sky while I look down upon a rich forest. When we burst through the clouds, the horse becomes a dragon, and I ride the dragon above the clouds until it vanishes completely.

Now, I'm gliding alone. I dip down below the clouds and sail towards the treetops. As I approach the trees, a bee appears in front of me. Either the bee is a giant or I am tiny because we are the same size. The bee shows me a path, and I fly behind it for a while. We dip down through the canopy and then down further to the forest floor. When I reach the earth, an enormous snake appears before me, and we slide together through the undergrowth. The snake is monstrous, and on its head is now perched a bulbous frog. The snake takes me through the darkness, then drops me off in a clearing at the base of the cliff. At the top of the cliff is another white wolf. I call out and when the animal arrives at my side it is no longer a wolf, but a black and white sheep dog. I ask the dog if it is my power animal and it licks my face. We run together into the countryside until we come to a farm where I can live out my dream of growing my own food like my papou and raising a family away from the horrors of the city.

After the vision quest, Charlie and I sit back down by the pile of coca, and I describe to him what I experienced. Charlie mentions that the rabbits represent fear of going into the subconscious. The horse, he says, represents power. He nods and chews as I reel through the myriad of other creatures. When I mention the bee, he smiles and says that a bee had actually flown in, circled the room, and then landed on my forehead.

'You're pulling my leg,' I say, instinctively checking my head and face.

'Cross my heart, Nicholas. This is what we deal with here. Now Nick,' he says, sifting through the coca for the leaves he desires, 'it seems to me like you're not allowing for a natural flow of energy through your body. Too much up here,' he says, pointing to his forehead, 'and not enough here,' he points to his heart, 'and here,' he says, pointing to his belly.

'That's what Tony said in my last ceremony. And Paulo said it in my first ceremony. Something inside me is blocking my emotions.'

Charlie nods and chews. 'Your third chakra,' he says, tapping his belly, 'holds your emotions, your feelings. This is what we're clearing out.'

'I don't really understand.'

'You will,' says Charlie.

I leave the ceremony feeling energised and healthy and walk to the Big House to put my name down on the whiteboard for the next kambo ceremony.

*

The next day I find a moment to speak with Tony upstairs at the Big House. We recline on bean bags and smoke mapachos. He's wearing a button up shirt with sweat patches under his armpits. I give him a similar summary as I did to Charlie of my path to Way of the Spirit, my crossroads and my experiences with ayahuasca. Tony speaks directly, with eyes that penetrate. Sometimes the beginnings of a smile cracks through the side of his mouth, where his thick mapacho hangs like a gangster's cigar.

'Have you sat with tobacco?' he asks.

'Paulo brewed up a diet for me and the boys.'

'I recommend another one,' he says. 'My tobacco is stronger than Paulo's.'

Sounds a little ominous… 'Okay, I'm in.'

'Great. Solitude is best when you're on diet. It's essential, really, to go into your process and really feel what comes up.'

'In that case, maybe I'd be better off waiting until my friends Billy and Stan leave for home so that I can be alone. They're leaving on Saturday.'

'That's probably a good idea.'

'I'm thinking of extending my stay another week as well.'

Tony nods. 'I'll talk with Isabella to see if we have the space. See you in the Maloka tonight.'

*

I felt the medicine coming on after my first cup but went up for a second almost out of habit. Tony casually pushed his bucket towards me after I gagged at the smell. The medicine fizzed in my mouth like kombucha. Thick, muddy, dirt kombucha. It's hard to believe, but the taste of the ayahuasca is becoming nastier.

Now the Maloka is completely dark, and water trickles out of my eyes and escapes from the corners of my mouth. My body is heavy and melting and lying limp on the mat. My head is thick with confusion and worry. The medicine is pushing down, down, down, deep down below the floor.

The drumbeat of blood in my eardrums.

I know that it's time…

Inhale.

Exhale.

I can hear it coming…

The *Language*!

Thandros! Thanatos!

Thralling. Thromping. Thrain!

Oh God! I'm at the threshold. To tip over the edge means entering the DMT Realm.

I don't know if I can handle this again!

Fear! Oh God, the Fear!

Whatever it is that I am walks the tightrope between this realm and the chaos and the madness that awaits on the other side.

A voice: *You don't have to go there if you don't want to, my son.*

I'm afraid. The threshold dissolves. The DMT Realm fades until I'm Nicholas again, lying on the mat.

Coward.

*

I shuffle along in the dark towards the bathroom to void the dreadful, uncomfortable feeling in my guts. I click on my torch and step into a cubicle, swinging the door shut behind me. I hold my torch in my mouth and sit on the toilet. Before I've finished scanning for spiders, the liquid begins to hurtle out of my arse. The purge is still gushing out of me when the toilet door begins to pulse.

I don't want to spend the night in this cubicle. I don't want to be trapped in here. Oh shit. Which cubicle am I in? Am I in number one? I think I am. Oh horror! I don't want to spend eternity in cubicle number one!

Come on, man, really? Jasper is full of shit.

I quickly wipe my arse and fill the toilet bucket with the powdered wood chips, trying my best to avoid all the black snakes slithering into the bowl from the fractures in the floor. I stumble out of the cubicle and over to the basin where I frantically clean my hands and then race back to my mat and slump down with my right forearm against my mat, holding my body up while I lean over my bucket. It's just a matter of time now. The universe begins to spiral around me. I am a black hole. The *Language* whispers in my ears. …*thandros… thanatos…*

thralling… thromping… thrain… An eruption from deep in my belly. And I purge into my bucket. *All my fears! All my fears! All my fears!* The black snakes pour out from my belly and out of my mouth and into the bucket along with all of my fears, until exhausted, I lie back down on my mat and curl up and close my eyes.

By the close of the ceremony, I'm out of the medicine. I ask the boys how their night was, and Stan admits that he spent most of it in tears.

'I gotta go back to Casa del Graham,' he says.

Billy and I hang back at the Maloka a little while longer.

'Anything come up for you tonight, mate?' I ask.

'Not really. Another night feeling stoned and crook until I spewed.'

I light up a mapacho and take a long draw.

'That'll do it as far as ceremonies go for me, mate,' says Billy. 'The next one's scheduled for the night before me and Stan fly out, so I reckon we'll just leave it at that.'

'Did you get much from the experience?'

'Not a whole lot. I guess I just don't have too many demons hidden inside,' he says.

'Could be.'

'Or maybe they're just hidden *really* well.'

*

Early morning sunshine illuminates the Maloka. The light dances off the central star pentagram carved into the polished wooden floorboards and fills the space up to the spider's web of wooden beams in the ceiling. A dozen soft mats lie around the perimeter of the space, with bodies occupying a few of them. I take a draw from my mapacho then lay it to rest in my little wooden bowl. Stan's already lying down in the foetal position. Billy is purging into his bucket. There's a new girl with caramel skin and wild curly hair sitting on the mat next to me doing pranayama breathwork.

Tony squats beside me. Droplets of sweat trickle down his cheeks. 'How are you feeling, Nick?'

'A little nervous,' I say.

Tony smiles and then it's five burns on the fleshy part of my right shoulder with the smouldering end of his incense stick. Onto the wounds he heaps frog poison paste. My heartrate explodes, and my neck and face are hot with panic. The blood pounds against my temples from the inside of my skull. Hot mouth and impending doom. All the moisture has left my throat. My body is shutting down, getting ready to give it all away. I have just a second to grab my bucket before a cascade of burning bile and water floods out of my mouth. My stomach heaves and a second purge comes, violent and painful and gut-wrenching. I slump down onto my mat to rest for a few moments. The blood pumps at my shoulder. The poison is still there feeding into my open wound.

Shit! I've got to get to the bathroom!

I take my bucket and drag myself into the first cubicle. After stripping off my clothes I sit naked on the toilet, purging from both ends, with the bucket wedged between my legs.

'This sucks,' comes Billy's voice. He must be in the cubicle next to me.

'How's it going in there?' I splutter.

'Is that you, Nicko?'

'Yeah, mate.'

'I'm purging out both ends.'

'Me too.'

'Why did we *do* this?'

But soon I'm out of the worst of it. I leave the bathroom and lie back down on my mat. Tony wipes off the poison. I curl into a ball.

At the Big House, Esmerelda the chef washes our wounds and dabs them with Betadine. When she's finished patching up the wounded guests, Esmerelda, with help from her team of young workers, ferries out a typically tantalising banquet for lunch. There's potato stew with white beans, garden salad with fresh herbs, parboiled green beans, roasted root vegetables, two bowls of special spicy sauce and three jugs of freshly squeezed fruit juice. The spread looks incredible, but we've all been knocked around so heavily by the kambo that none of us manage more than a few mouthfuls.

After lunch, I lounge about shirtless upstairs with Billy and Stan. My kambo wound throbs. It looks like someone rolled a five on a dice and then branded it into my shoulder. I light a mapacho and watch the smoke swirl around my face. Ants crawl around the floor, and geckos fumble across the flywire walls. Stan gets up from his beanbag and walks along by the bookshelf then sits down and stares out into the trees. I finish my mapacho and sit on the floor next to him. 'You alright?'

'Yeah, I'm alright, mate,' he says. 'It's just been a rough couple of days. That kambo hit me pretty fucken hard this morning. I thought I was really dying.' Stan looks out into the trees. 'Plus, my missus is pissed at me because I didn't tell her I'd be out of phone contact. She thinks I don't give a shit about her. I miss her so much and she doesn't even know it. The last aya ceremony was rough for me as well. I didn't have any visions. I didn't even feel like purging. I just felt empty. Maybe it was punishment. I spent most of that ceremony crying. And feeling super, super sad.'

I lean over and give the big guy a hug.

Chapter Thirteen
Farewell

It's breakfast time and there's a pile of shoes outside the Big House and a hive of activity inside. This is the busiest I've seen the place. Sam, the guy who helped me through my second ceremony, is smoking a mapacho and next to him, Jasper is talking about fucking goddamned cubicle number one. I introduce myself to a couple of new guys and then shuffle my way around the table to say good morning to Isabella. She says there's space for me at Way of the Spirit for as long as I want to stay, then she introduces me to her friend Ellie, the caramel-skinned girl with wild black hair and a Caribbean accent.

'Pleased to meet you, Ellie,' I say, infatuated.

After breakfast, Billy and Stan ask the table for advice on the best place to eat meat in town. 'We're heading home on Saturday,' says Billy, 'so we're rewarding ourselves.'

The ayahuasca diet is supposed to continue for a couple of weeks after your last ceremony. I consider reminding my friends of this, and can see the same thoughts going through

Isabella's mind, but instead I ask if anyone would like to join us on a trip into town.

While Billy and Stan eat meat at a Texas BBQ diner, Sam leads Ellie and me on the footpath towards the Belen Markets. It's surreal looking to my left, out past the marshes and the sprawling shanty town, to the mighty Amazon River. As a boy, I'd devoured pulp adventure novels about the Amazon. About fearless explorers searching and braving anacondas and caiman for gold or fame. About evil slave traders and rubber barons, and Indigenous tribes untouched by Europeans. To the right of the footpath, the buildings have the appearance of old colonial-style ruins. I imagine Iquitos as a booming port-city and conjure images of hot, sweaty nights filled with music and liquor and whores and sailors.

At the end of the path, we come to the Belen Markets, and Sam advises we pay attention to our pockets. 'It's rare there's any violence here,' he says, in his typical measured tone. 'At night it's a different story.'

I slam into a wall of putrid stench, of degraded rubbish and piss and petrol. Food scraps line the muddy and potholed streets. Raw meat is out in the open air, with flies swarming the flesh. There are vultures on the roofs, writhing in alarming black masses, jostling for position and poised to feed on scraps. We pass down alleyways with long lines of white tables, stacked with tropical fruits and vegetables and dried meats and beans. Fat river fish lie gutted and splayed out on long wooden tables.

Down a side street, past a line of plastic-trinket lanes, and we are in the Witches Alley. All manner of potions and herbs are here: powdered San Pedro cactus, bottles of pre-made ayahuasca, toé, tobacco brews, mapacho, bunches of fresh herbs, bottles of pickled herbs and roots. We stock up on mapacho, Palo Santo, chocolate balls and *Agua de Florida*, and then we push our way back out of the chaos of the markets and onto the boardwalk, which is quiet, save for a few groups of school children in uniform and the odd strange looking shirtless man. When we reach the main drag, the street people come out. There are young men and women with dreadlocks selling psychedelic prints, clothing and nut carvings. Dark-skinned men in hats sell trinkets and drugs. Junkies lie on park benches, and next to them, women in tribal garb sell paintings. At Dawn on the Amazon, the place with the best vegetables, juices and WIFI in town, I order a salad from the 'Ayahuasca Diet Menu' and send messages to my friends and family, while we wait for Billy and Stan to return from their meat expedition.

'I won't come back to town in a hurry,' I say to Ellie and Sam. They just nod their heads. This has been a painful reminder of what the outside world feels like. The sounds, the cars, the people, the intensity, the sickness, the pollution. It doesn't feel good. It feels like poison...

*

A rainstorm claps in the shining violet distance, and the white-blue glow of the moon casts menacing shadows across the winding pathway as I scamper – still twisted and afraid – along the wooden planks from the Maloka towards Casa del Graham. Warm, heavy raindrops spit at me through breaches in the canopy. This jungle is bright and alive, the night unsettlingly radiant. I twist and turn through the tunnels until I reach the safety of home.

I am certainly not out of the medicine, even now, and probably should've stayed on my mat, but Isabella was with Ellie and one of the other girls, and they were hugging and giggling. It was tormenting. I had to get out of there. Apart from those girls, it was all unfamiliar faces for my first ceremony without Billy and Stan.

I rustle around now looking for a match to light some candles on the bookshelf. Something large brushes against my leg. Startled, I look down. 'Fuck! Jesus, Gaia. You scared the fuck outta me.'

'Oh yeah,' comes a croaky voice from behind Billy's mosquito net. 'Gaia came home with us after dinner.'

The storm cracks on outside as I sit on the rocking chair, bucket at my feet and two-litre plastic water bottle in my lap. Gaia's asleep on the floor next to me. My power animal. She stays with me during my endless trips back and forth from the bathroom. It takes seven, maybe ten, watery tap-arse butt-purges before I finally clear it all out. I'd sit down on the toilet and shit, feel as though all the medicine was purged, wipe my arse and stand, motion towards the basin to wash my hands when, *oh fuck there's more*, and I'd do a little jiggle dance and sit back down again.

It seems like the ayahuasca is cleaning out my insides, grabbing all the ancient shit in there and flushing it away. I just wish it'd hurry the fuck up about it.

I lost my nerve in the Maloka tonight. I stood at the razor's edge of the DMT Realm. I peered into the abyss. Glimpsed the Horror. And I pulled back again. The DMT Realm dissolved, and I lay on my mat, relieved and disappointed. Safe. But still a coward.

And now, as I lie in my bed contemplating my cowardice, the medicine returns like a holographic jester from behind the theatre curtains. A fog of threatening madness washing over me. When I close my eyes, there come gentle rolling visionscapes. And there are faint murmurings of the Language.

In the distance it whispers: *thrall*... shhhh... It's like an aftershock of the Language, or a reverberation, bouncing off the walls of my skull: *thana*... *thana*... dewbie dewbie... *thanathos*... shhhh... It's a dancing, flipping, boomeranging echo of the Language. It's as though the Language first blasted through my consciousness and then it vibrated out, and when it collided with the boundaries of the universe that is my mind, it bounced back, like sound waves in a cave, and returned, diminished but familiar. And so here it is now, faint echoes from the walls of the cave of my consciousness. *Thana*... *thana*... dewbie dewbie... *thanathos*... shhhh...

The experience wouldn't be so frightening, except for one lingering thought: *What if the medicine never ends?*

*

I split my cold weather gear and other non-essential items into two bags and give one each to Billy and Stan to take back to Perth with them, then we catch a boat into town. I hug my brothers by the filthy shores and tell them I love them, then jump into a taxi headed for Dawn on the Amazon.

And that's that. I'm on my own again. It's alright. I'm excited. It won't be long before I'm leaving this place myself and carrying on with my journey. So, I never ended up meeting God, or aliens. I'm still satisfied with my experience. I haven't really been smashed apart by the medicine since that second ceremony. It rattled me, that experience, no point denying it. And if I'm honest with myself, I've been too shit-scared to go that deep again. That one special night was enough, I guess.

The taxi driver drops me off and I slide past the usual suspects flogging their wares. Next door to Dawn on the Amazon is a small office with an open door, and there's an old guy sitting out the front of the office on a white plastic chair with a skipper's hat and a broad smile. I give him a little chin nod like I'm a local around these parts.

Inside, I order the green salad and a camu-camu juice then slowly sort out some more of my journey to Costa Rica. I've arranged to leave Way of the Spirit on the first of August and I've booked one night in Iquitos at Hotel La Casona. I'll catch a boat from Iquitos to Santa Rosa, where Peru meets the borders of both Colombia and Brazil, and I'll stay two nights in Leticia, on the Colombian side of the border, before flying further north to Bogota. I'm yet to lock in the rest of my steps to Costa Rica, where I'll meet Craig and his mate Glassy, but that'll have to wait till next time, because I've had enough of the internet and the fucking city for today.

*

The light of the morning sun pours in through the flywire walls of Casa del Graham. Outside, a troop of large grey monkeys tear through the treetops sending leaves and branches and fruit husks crashing to the ground. I run my hands over the naked flesh of my chest as beads of sweat begin to form on my skin. I stink of the jungle. I don't bother putting a shirt on. The cleaners drop into my house just as I'm leaving for breakfast. I ask them to remake Billy's old bed so I can sleep there. At breakfast, I smile to the girls from the last ceremony. They're sitting together like a schoolyard clique.

'It sounded like you all had a nice ceremony the other night,' I say. 'There was a bit of a giggle-fest going on there at the end.'

They laugh. 'Oh my God, I'm sorry,' says Ellie. 'I hope we didn't take you out of your process?'

'Nah,' I reply. 'It was cute. To be honest, I was a little bit jealous.'

After breakfast, I arrange my clothes across my old bed, and spend the rest of the day reading and writing. In the fading light of the evening, I walk with Gaia and Sam, the lean-bodied Canadian, towards the Maloka. Ellie joins the wooden path from up ahead of us and skips along on her own.

'Hey guys,' she cries, quickly dropping to the ground. 'Come check this out.' She's hovering above something on the path. 'Look how beautiful it is.'

I approach and lean in over her, to see a small tarantula, frozen on the path.

'It's a baby, right?' she says.

'Looks like it,' I say.

'I'd rather not meet the mother,' says Sam.

Gaia pokes her head between us but seems uninterested in the spider.

I sit with my back against the wall of the Maloka and light up a mapacho. I like to smoke a mapacho while I wait for everyone to arrive. I also like to smoke a little just before I go up to drink the brew; it helps calm my nerves and to bring me into focus. I like to smoke a little more when I return to my mat to ward off some of the initial nausea of the medicine. Outside of ceremony, I like to smoke a mapacho when writing my notes; it makes me feel like Hunter S. Thompson. When I leave this place, I'll stop.

*

Again, I find myself escaping along the wooden path back to Casa del Graham, not quite out of the medicine, and yet unwilling to stay any longer in the Maloka. During my shamanic reading, Tony took my pulse and felt my abdomen. 'Your energy is good,' he said. 'You have a strong connection with the medicine but there's still emotion in your body that your mind is blocking you from dealing with. I'm brewing you up a tobacco diet that's going to help with this.'

I take a left turn off the main path and head on for Casa del Graham. White-blue shadow spirits glide around the trees. Soft imitations of the Language dance around the back garden of my mind. It's like some part of my mind is trying to bring on the DMT Realm, or perhaps it's playing tricks on me. Either way, this is a concerning development. *Wait… Did I take the right turn-off? What if a space-time portal opens in the jungle before I get home? What if I make it happen just by thinking it?*

I take a mapacho from my pocket, light it up and softly draw in the smoke.

Chill out, Nick, for fuck's sake.

When Paulo sang his final icaro tonight, as usual, the medicine kicked up a gear for me. I curled into a ball and rode it out for a while. Sometime later, when I lifted my head from the mat there was a small gathering of people left in the Maloka. Isabella was sharing a mat with one of the new guys, who I now assume has been here before. Sam and Ellie were there as well. And a few others I didn't recognise. Ellie turned to face me and smiled, then gestured for me to come over. I stayed for a little while and listened to the others, not wanting to isolate myself now that Billy and Stan have gone, but when my stomach gurgled, I took this as my cue to leave. Now I'm approaching Casa del Graham, and my stomach's going bonkers. I don't feel comfortable purging in the Maloka; there's something about being trapped in the bathrooms that still haunts me. Jasper and his goddamn cubicle number one. And I feel weird about going to the bathroom while everyone's lucid and hanging out on the mats chatting. Now that I'm safe at home I rush straight for the toilet, sit down and turn on the tap-arse. I've almost made it over to the sink when I get the signal from my bowels to sit back down again. I take to jiggling and dancing around naked in my bathroom to encourage every last drop of liquid to squirt its way out of my bowels. I wash my hands thoroughly then induce vomit, shower and brush my teeth, then change into some cotton boxers. I'm just about to clamber into bed when I notice that I have a guest in my house. Standing by the door, looking up at me with a curious, expectant grin, is a lean-bodied, yellow-haired mutt.

'Did you let yourself in?'

She looks at me, then eyes my old single bed. She sits down and thumps her tail against the ground.

'I'm gonna call you Dingo. How's that sound?'

She looks at my old bed again. I shake my head. Dingo yelps. I shake my head again. She huffs at me, then trots upstairs. I wonder if it's any coincidence that she's turned up the day after the boys left. I potter around in the living room a little longer. Later, I find her passed out on Stan's old bed.

In the morning, Dingo appears at my feet with her tail between her legs, her head down and her feet tip-tapping nervously on the floor. She drops down and rolls onto her back. I give her a tummy scratch but tell her she can't stay here permanently. Something about her is off.

After breakfast, I walk with Ellie along the path back to our houses, with the two dogs ahead of us chasing chickens.

'Gaia and Dingo have both slept at my place now,' I say. 'Dingo stayed over last night.'

'Wait,' she says giggling, 'who is Dingo?'

'I don't know her name. But she's that one,' I say pointing, 'with the short yellow hair.'

'Her name is Shobi.'

'She looks like a dingo from the Australian outback.'

'Gaia used to stay at my place all the time,' says Ellie. 'But not Shobi. I don't like her. I think she has had some trauma in her life.'

I smile and nod. Dingo tears after a chicken into the jungle. Gaia loses interest and trots behind me and Ellie.

*

It's dinner time in the Big House, and the folks who've been drinking San Pedro all day are rolling around the dining room giggling and melting into the seats.

When the kitchen staff finish cleaning and bid us goodnight, Ellie and I join the others in the Maloka. We drag the mats into the middle of the room and lay down and hang out. I feel far more comfortable than last night, not having all those litres of shit built up in my guts waiting to explode out. One of the guys plays music with his Bluetooth speakers, and he passes around some mixed nuts. I lie next to Ellie and we both stare up at the spider-web ceiling. Ellie says she's going to be staying here a while longer, at least another three months.

'Tony said I can take a job here when I'm ready,' she says. 'I am fascinated by this work.'

'That sounds amazing,' I say. 'I've extended my stay until the first of August.'

'That's cool. So, you like it?'

'Well, I think I've figured out what I'm doing here.'

'Oh yeah?'

'All my life I've felt I was missing something. That there was more to this life. I looked out at the world as a young man and thought: *this can't be it?*'

'Sure, okay.'

'I was afraid that this life was all a big nothing. No point to anything. No beauty. Just dull, boring, pointless, bullshit. But all the while, I've had this inkling, this faint sense of hope, that the world was not as boring and lame as it seemed, that in fact, the world was enchanted. That magic is real. Gods and spirits and love and fairies. All of it is real. And so that's what I'm doing here. I'm here to test my hypothesis: that the world is magical.'

'That's great,' she says, turning to face me. 'I love magic!'

'Ellie, we are soldiers in the war between the magical and the mundane.'

She laughs.

What I said wasn't really meant to be funny, but it's okay, because there is nothing greater in the world than the laughter of a beautiful woman.

Chapter Fourteen
More Tobacco

Tony shakes a big plastic bottle then cracks the top off.

'My tobacco is more concentrated than Paulo's,' he says with a grin. We're sitting opposite each other on the floor of Graham. I have a bucket to my right and a bottle of water to my left. Tony pours a dose of the light brown, soy-sauce-looking brew into a small white soup bowl. He blows tobacco smoke from his giant mapacho over the liquid, then prays in Spanish and holds the bowl out towards me.

'It's best to get it all down in one go,' he says, as I bring the tobacco to my face. I drink it all down. Tastes of soggy cigarette butts, garlic, soy sauce, black pepper and fire.

'So, I shouldn't fight it,' I say, 'if it wants to come up straight away?'

'That's alright. Just breathe.'

There's a tingling in my fingers as I hold my right hand over my belly.

'Try to sit with your feelings today,' says Tony. 'Meditate. And write down what comes up.'

Tony leaves and I purge the tobacco into my bucket. Soon after, Ellie passes by my house. Ellie's staying in Fleur, about fifty metres further along the wooden path from my place. Fleur is the most secluded of the houses at Way of the Spirit.

'Morning,' I say, through the flywire walls.

'You are on diet?' she calls from the path.

'Just got my first drink down.'

'Do you need anything? Do you have enough water?'

'I'm okay, thanks.'

'Just let me know if you do.'

Wednesday will be Ellie's last ceremony before going into diet. I've set my intention for Wednesday night to stay in the Maloka after the ceremony and sit with whoever is there. I don't want to bring any fear or purge with me back to Casa del Graham. I want to let it all go in the Maloka.

It's early afternoon when Tony returns with more tobacco. I breathe through the initial nausea, this time keeping it down.

'How's it going then?' asks Tony, slinging himself into my hammock.

'Can we talk about alcohol?'

'I think we should.'

'I enjoy the feeling of being drunk,' I say. 'I like the bonding experience of drinking with friends. I actually like the feeling of losing control. When I was younger, I liked the way it made me a more fun and interesting person, and the way it helped me to let go of social anxiety. But these days it takes a brutal toll.' I take a drag from my mapacho. 'I find it hard to stop once I start drinking. And then when I'm drunk, I'll revert to certain behaviours that are not good for me, like eating shit food or just drinking more. And then I find myself acting stupidly or saying stupid things. But the main issue is the destructive effect on my body. I know it's slowing me down, holding me back from achieving what I want in the world. I know it's slowly killing me. I was thinking maybe I need to quit drinking.'

'Be careful with that idea.'

'But this ayahuasca diet prohibits alcohol. What about purifying the body and all that?'

'While you're sitting with the medicine it's very important to follow the diet. But purification can isolate you from the world, and that's not a good thing. You still want to be a social animal, Nick. You just need to learn self-control. It's okay to drink alcohol. But make sure that *you* are in control. Use alcohol to stay grounded. Use it to live in this world. But do it *consciously*, and *purposefully*. Try to reduce that casual attitude to drinking. Drink wine with your meal if the occasion calls for it but stay in control. If you're going to get drunk with your friends, *do it*, but make it occasional, and make it ceremonial. Treat it like a medicine and make it a ritual.'

Tony shuffles around in his hammock. I take a sip of water from my bottle.

'I can't figure out if I should go back to Perth. It's where I grew up. When I'm there, though, I find myself returning to unhealthy behaviour patterns. Each time I travel I go through this deep personal change and find it difficult to relate to my friends and my family when I return home. On the outside, obviously, I seem like my old self but on the inside, I'm different. Nobody over there understands me, so I get frustrated and give up. I slide backwards, then I get agitated and want to leave again.'

Tony dabs the sweat from his head with a handkerchief.

'I'm not sure if I mentioned before,' I say, 'but I had a bit of an emotional breakdown at the start of my trip. I missed my family. I was really depressed. And then I felt guilty about feeling depressed.'

'Sounds like loneliness to me. Loneliness is being incomplete in the self. It's needing others to fill the space inside. You were by yourself at the start of your trip, right?'

'Yes.'

'Well, what if you projected your feelings of loneliness onto your family. You were scared to be alone with yourself, and so it appeared to you like you missed your family. You're doing it again now. Your friends have left, and you're alone again. And *now* you miss your family and your friends back home. Look,' he says shaking his head a little, 'it's great to love your family. It's great to have a good relationship with them. But you don't want to *miss* them. You don't want to *miss* anyone.'

Tony leans over to ash out his mapacho in my spew bucket.

'Do you have a regular meditation practice?' he asks.

I squirm a little and scratch my head. 'I've tried a bunch of times to keep one. I can do it for a few weeks. And then I stop for a few months.'

Tony nods. 'It's probably the most important change you could make to your life to have a daily meditation practice. The idea is to learn how to observe the thoughts that come up in your mind, and to let them go without attaching to them. You want to be able to make decisions and act from a place of groundedness. If your thoughts take control of your mind, you can become trapped making decisions from fear. Learn how to bring yourself back to a stable baseline, a place of calm, grateful contentedness. And train yourself to do it every day. Meditation is important for us because it moves us away from attachment to desire. In the Buddhist tradition, to live without attachment to desire is to live without suffering. Cultivate this discipline within yourself and you'll be surprised how powerful it is.'

I smile.

He leaves.

I don't understand.

I take out my notebook and pen and try to get to the bottom of the situation. There's a movement in the new-age community around 'manifestation'. You have a goal, or an intention, or a desire, and you focus on it every day, and eventually it will manifest in your life. But how does this sit with the Buddhist teaching that desire leads to suffering? Are these not contradictory ideas?

I pause from my notes to purge into my bucket. I notice a pressure in my stomach, in the lower centre of my ribcage. I can feel my blood beating there.

Whenever I think about my intentions for this life, the most powerful and consistent idea coming up is my dream to be a published writer. I want it so fucking bad that it hurts. I want to have my work read by others. I want to have an impact on the world. I want to contribute to the artistic community. I want girls to read my books and tell me that it made them feel things. I want people to tell me that my writing is good. I want to devote myself to my passion, without the strain and the stress and the pain of doing some other work to keep myself alive. I want to put food on the table doing something I actually love… I sit with this vision for just a moment. A profound wave of gratitude passes through my bones and warms each muscle and organ of my body, and I realise that my life is beautiful.

*

Morning rays hit my face. I slip out of bed and scrub my body in the shower. The water is always cold here. The cold water brings me to life. While I'm brushing my teeth, a frog pokes its head out of the tap in the bathroom. Last night there was a storm in the jungle, and now the world around me is softer, wetter, fresher and somehow calmer. I fold into the hammock and light a mapacho. The smoke dances around my face.

When Tony arrives, we both take a seat on the floor. I take down my third bowl of medicine. Tony looks to me expectantly. I light a mapacho and take a long inhale, holding my little brown ash bowl in my lap.

'I've been thinking about women. A lot.'

'Have you remained continent here?' he asks. 'Holding your energy?'

'I have.'

'Good. Keep that up. You need your energy.'

'It's hard.'

'I'm sure it is.'

'I think I'm ready for a committed relationship. I've been in a series of short-term casual relationships for the past year or so. And it's been fun. But I feel like I want to share my life with someone. Share my dreams. I want to really grow with someone and help them grow. But I – I'm afraid I'll just fuck it up.'

'Yesterday we talked about you being lonely and depressed. And *now* you say you're ready for a committed relationship. Can you see what's going on? You don't want to need someone else to feel complete, to feel whole, to feel happy.' Tony shuffles around so both his feet are planted into the ground. 'You gotta get straight with that before you get into a relationship. Or else you'll be using a woman to fill the hole inside you. And that'll never work. You've got to be content in the self, wanting and needing nothing from others. Then you can *choose* to be with someone.' Tony takes a draw from his giant mapacho, then he leans out of the hammock, stands and grabs his backpack. 'How are you feeling?'

'I feel good. A lot to process.'

He smiles and slips his pack onto his back. 'I'll see you this afternoon.'

In the late morning, I induce vomit and afterwards feel very weak. I try to keep writing my notes but find it too taxing, so start reading Kurt Vonnegut's *Cat's Cradle* in the hammock with a mapacho smouldering away in my lips. I found this book upstairs at the Big House when I'd finished *Slaughterhouse-Five*.

I love this writer.

I'm in love with this mapacho.

I'm in love with the world.

Ellie walks past and stops for a chat through the fly screen. Golden, caramel skin. Black hair, thick and wild. Vibrant, energetic, feminine.

I'm in love with Ellie.

To think, I was supposed to be leaving Way of the Spirit today...

Tony returns in the late afternoon. Before he pours my fourth cup of tobacco, I ask him about my 'desire and suffering' dilemma.

'It's the *attachment* to desire that brings suffering,' he says. 'Clear your mind so that you can access your unconscious from a place of gratitude rather than fear. Acknowledge your inner desire. Set your intention. And then let it go. If you operate from a place of gratitude, then you are always content, and you'll find an ease to life. If you attach yourself to specific outcomes and operate from a place of lacking, of wanting, of wishing, then you'll find only suffering.'

'That makes sense.'

'If nothing else, have gratitude as a practice.'

Tony shuffles his position in the hammock so that his legs are stretched out straight. He looks up at the ceiling then turns back to face me. 'Are you familiar with the concept of visualising abundance?'

'Is that like, *fake it till you make it*?'

He grins. 'You could say that. Think about these goals of yours. Bring them into your mind. Focus on how they make you *feel*. Sit with that feeling in your body. Try to hold the feeling. And then realise that you can bring that feeling into your body at any time.'

'I guess my goals are kind of all over the place. I know that I want to be a writer. I kind of hate being a teacher. But then I don't know how I'm gonna earn a living. I don't even know where I'm gonna live. I feel like I can't really be myself in Perth.'

Tony takes the mapacho out of his mouth. 'You do realise that it's not the place that's the problem, Nicholas. It's not Perth. It's not your friends or your family. It's *you*. Whether you're travelling or at home, it's still you. It's always you.'

My face is blank with resistance.

'Wherever I go,' he says, 'there I am.'

I try to let Tony's words sink in. He smiles and sticks his mapacho back in his mouth, lights it and exhales a plume of smoke into the air.

'Okay, how about this then,' says Tony. 'Do you find that you modify your behaviour around different people? That you're changing who you are at work, with your family, with your friends, when you're by yourself?'

I nod. 'Yeah sure. I can adapt who I am to many situations.'

'And how's that going for you?'

I chuckle. 'It's tiring. But I feel like it's a skill?'

163

'Sure, being adaptable is a skill. But you don't want to change yourself for someone else, because if you keep changing yourself, then you won't know who you are. I don't compromise who *I* am. It doesn't matter where I am, I speak my truth. How about you try to be true to yourself at *all* times.'

Tony pours the brew. I drink. He leaves. I purge.

And then I take some time to think about his words.

Nicholas. Nicky. Nicko. Nick. How many different people am I trying to be? I've been leading so many lives, playing so many roles, that I've forgotten who I actually am. Who is the person under all the layers? I play at being a party animal with my school friends but that's not me anymore. I don't think it ever was. I play at being a high school teacher, but I can't stand the education system. I play at being Australian, but I don't love the country I was born in. The country who still refuses to make amends with its shameful past. I'm a mongrel whose blood is Greek, English and Irish and I don't identify with any of those cultures. I can't talk with my family about psychedelics because they think I'm a junky. I pretend to give a shit about the news, about the economy, about politics, about sports, about social media, but really, I don't care about any of it. I just wish everyone would shut the fuck up and leave me alone.

But what *do* I care about? What *do* I live for? Why do I even bother getting up in the morning? I know there's a reason. Even if it isn't immediately clear. I know there's something more to this life. I've caught glimpses of it. I felt it at Machu Picchu, if only for a fleeting moment. I've felt it here in the jungle. Fuck. I experienced it in all its shocking glory during my second ceremony. I know that it's there, the great… 'it'. But what *is* 'it'? I don't know yet. But I'm close.

*

I've showered and brushed my teeth and am ready to crawl into bed when I notice Shobi and Gaia scratching at my front door. It seems that with Stan and Billy gone, Casa del Graham has become an open house. Party time. Open for squatters. They look quizzically at me when they can't push the door open. An entitled huff. A frustrated grumble. *Sorry ladies, I need to be on my own tonight...*

*

The fifth cup of tobacco went down and came back up a few minutes later. It was a tough spew coming from deep in my belly. I felt it vibrating in that section between my belly button and that soft bone that's appeared at the base of the sternum. Tony stuck around to watch me purge, wished me good luck for tonight's ayahuasca ceremony, then departed.

Still seated on the floor, I wipe my face and slide a mapacho between my lips. That's it for the tobacco diet, thank fuck. I lie down on my bed to try a meditation technique Tony showed me. I breathe in deeply, then visualise my breath moving from my right shoulder, out through my right hand. I repeat this nine times, and then change to my left shoulder and hand. I visualise my breath moving from my right hip, down my leg and out through my right foot. Then the left. I breath into my abdomen and exhale through my chest and up out of the top of my head. My spine shivers. My skin tingles. A rush pulses up and down my body.

When I finish my meditation, I write a poem in my journal.

La Purga

Days in isolation

165

La dieta
Purge the burning liquid
Day after day in introspection
Night falls and I walk my path alone
Quietly, I sit until my name is called
Then down it goes, another cup
I've done it now, no turning back
An age passes as the icaros meld into my mind
I wait
I wait
Another cup, vile as the last
And again, I wait
I wait with my doubts
She comes in waves. She searches me
My skin is alive
I can feel her now
I approach the threshold
The precipice between this world and the next
A world of light and jewels
To go there I must leave the self behind
'Would you like to enter?' she asks
Yes.
Language collapses. Reality collapses.
This is infinity!
This is Eternity!
The Horror! Too much to bear!
I am back in the room now
But the people are strange...
I know not what I am
This is insanity. This is insanity.
I am trapped
I will never get out

The sickness is building
My body shudders
I grasp the bucket
Here it comes. Here it comes. Here it comes. Here it comes…
The purge
I'm back. I am I
Connected to Source
Ecstasy
Euphoria
I've never felt more real. I've never felt more alive
Alive
I am alive

*

I lie on my back and wonder when the medicine will arrive. I notice my thoughts drifting to old memories. Sucking my thumb as a young boy. Wetting the bed and the shameful walk up the hallway to my parents' room. Then my chewing phase. I used to chew the collars of my school shirts like a rat until I'd worn through them. I started taking a hand towel to school so I could chew that instead of my collar. I bit some kid at playgroup. I remember when I pissed on Timmy McVaney's 'going-out' shoes on the way home from school. I don't remember why I did it. We were just kids at the time. There were maybe five of us there. The others didn't hold him down or anything. They just watched.

It's not until the candles are flickering that the medicine really begins to take hold. I try to fight it, so I can keep my intention to talk with the people in the Maloka, but it's no use. I dig my head into the pillow and surrender.

People are moving. Some are talking, some are leaving. Someone comes to check on me, and I tell their shadow that I'm okay. The room spins, and my body sinks deeper and deeper into the mat. Streams of salt liquid squeeze a path down my cheeks. Black clouds invade my consciousness. No more memories of childhood. Just darkness and doubt and fear and confusion. Head in the pillow. Ride it out.

There are a few bodies left in the Maloka. I pull myself together and sit with them. I can't really follow the conversation, so I just smile and nod. I'm almost out of the medicine. But I'm exhausted. The others want to leave for bed. Saliva floods my mouth.

'I just have to go to the bathroom to spew,' I mumble. 'Do you guys mind waiting for me?'

'Sure,' someone says.

In the cubicle, with my pants around my ankles and a bucket between my legs, the medicine returns. The walls swell and pulse and sparkle and shimmer. A portal opens up in the centre of the wooden door. I hear the Language, though it's muffled. It's a slingshot tumbling rendition. *Thhhrranngggg! Thrandros*, it goes. Firing and spinning and somersaulting. *Drous. Drous. Thralll!* And now I'm purging from both ends. The Language morphs into feeling and it's growlsy, oozy, grolshy, frothy. And now blackness. Swirling, writhing worms coming out of the darkness. Worms. Black worms swarm up from my belly and cascade out of my mouth into the bucket. A final whip crack, *Thhhrranngggg!* And then I droop my head and let the saliva pour out of my mouth. I close my eyes and the skin of my face hangs like a mask.

Chapter Fifteen
Leaving Summer Camp

Esmerelda cuts the tobacco diet for me with a plate of salted chilli, a lime wedge and a prayer.

'*Muchos gracias*,' I say, then let myself be wrapped up in a hug. My first human contact in days.

'*Desayuno?*' she asks.

'*Si.* I am *muchos hambre.*'

In the dining room Isabella asks if I'm interested in joining a kambo ceremony this morning.

Fuck. That. 'Maybe next time,' I say.

'Well, I am going into town after breakfast,' she says. 'Would you like to join me?'

'Sure.'

Esmerelda emerges from the kitchen with a bowl of guacamole and a plate of bread with butter and fried eggs. I could cry.

After scoring mapacho and chocolate balls at the Belen Markets, Isabella and I head to Karma Café, just around the corner from Dawn on the Amazon. The walls of Karma are decorated with psychedelic artwork and it smells of incense, coffee and chocolate. I scan the room trying to figure out which patrons are ayahuasca tourists, and which are just regular tourists.

'It's nicer in here than Dawn,' I say, sitting next to Isabella on a couch. She's wearing a flowing dress and her hair looks especially long and dark as it drapes over her shoulders.

'Yes, but the internet is not as good.'

I wire some more of my money to Way of the Spirit for my extension, then order a juice, guacamole and a salad. Isabella orders pancakes.

'I get such cravings working at Way of the Spirit,' she says.

'What do you miss most from the outside world?'

'Pasta.'

'I suppose you would. How long's it been since you were in Italy?'

'I was there three months ago. I'll go back again after two more months here.'

I take a sip of fruit juice. It's cold and sweet and tangy. 'What does your family think about what you do here?'

'Mostly, they don't understand.'

'Is that hard for you? I'd like to be open about my ayahuasca experiences with everyone back home.'

'I don't really talk much with my family about anything. But I think it is best to share about ayahuasca, only with those people who are ready to hear it.'

'But don't you think it's important to get the message out there? I feel like yelling from the rooftops.'

'Some people aren't ready to hear about the medicine, Nicholas. And it's not my place to convince them to come here. I just work with people who feel drawn to this place.'

Isabella wolfs down her pancakes, stopping only to breathe and to say things like, 'Oh my God, I love pancakes.' She has one of those figures that makes her look like she has never eaten a carb in her life. Isabella suggests we shift to the stools at the front of the café so we can smoke. I buy some chocolate balls for us to share.

'I'm glad we got the opportunity to come here together,' I say, pulling up a stool. 'The only real time we get to talk is when I'm "in the medicine" and you're standing over me asking if I want a banana.' I take a long draw from my mapacho and ash out in the tray. 'So, what's the deal with Tony and Charlie? Are they old friends or business partners, or, what's the situation?'

'They met here in the jungle maybe ten years ago. Tony came here with a few of his friends. Some of those guys have houses at Way of the Spirit named after them.'

'Like Casa del Graham?'

'That's right. Tony trained for many years with a great ayahuascero. He learned many different plant medicines. He married a local woman and they have two daughters. Eventually, he decided to open Way of the Spirit. Tony has come from a background in nutrition and master plants and the medicine. Charlie has a background in shamanism. He trained in the UK with different teachers, until he decided to come to Peru to train with the shamans over here. This is where he learned to be a coca shaman. When he met Tony, they became friends, and then Charlie came to work at Way of the Spirit. He has a wife and daughter here in Iquitos as well.'

A group of older men walk past us on the other side of the road towards the pub on the corner.

'I hate these men,' says Isabella.

'You know them?'

'I've overheard their conversations before at Dawn. They are disgusting. They are here to drink alcohol and to fuck young girls. They are abusers. Many of the women who come to Way of the Spirit have been abused by men.' She taps her mapacho against the ashtray. 'Many of these women have been abused in childhood or their younger years, and that abuse is all that they know. Sometimes they repress the abuse, they don't deal with it, and it becomes their only pattern of relationships. It's a terrible situation.'

*

My fingers lightly brush over the kambo scabs on my shoulder. My ninth and final ayahuasca ceremony at Way of the Spirit is upon me. Time for my rituals. Light three candles and place one on the bookshelf, one on the spare chair and one on the floor. Lay my Maloka clothes out: long pants, long-sleeved shirt, underwear, socks. Gather my supplies: mapachos, torch, water bottle. Leave a second water bottle on the floor by my bed for when I return after ceremony. Shower. Dry by candle-light. Change into my ceremony clothes. Blow out the candles. Put my boots on outside.

Walk the path to the Maloka.

My eighth ayahuasca ceremony was mostly uneventful. It was after my day in town with Isabella. Going into Iquitos really took me out of my process. The morning after that ceremony I lay on my bed and stared at the ceiling for an hour, feeling empty, blank, lifeless.

A knot's been slowly tightening in my stomach. A tension in my throat as well, like something is trying to get up or down but is stuck. The reality of leaving Way of the Spirit is dawning on me. A few days ago, I was consumed with excitement for

Central America. But it's different now. I've only just started to feel like a part of this community, and now I have to go. It feels like I'm about to leave summer camp.

Isabella is leading the ceremony tonight. I ask her for a big cup to start. And another big one for seconds. And then, there is no doubt—I am in the medicine. An intense visual dreamscape opens to my mind's eye. Twisting fluorescent fractals and kaleidoscopic patterns. And now I can *feel* the medicine. I am *feeling* it! Really *feeling* it. I can feel the medicine all through my body. In my organs, on my skin, in my blood, in my brain, in my hair. It's like my whole body has been lifted by some great hand and lowered into a warm, enveloping pool of ayahuasca. The Language of the DMT Realm is present, but only in my mind's periphery, like elevator music, or like a classical string quartet playing at a fancy cocktail party. The words are doing their somersaults and back flips and slingshots but the whole thing doesn't have the same urgency as usual.

But I'm ripped out of my ayahuasca bath and thrust into the stark reality of the Maloka. We are all connected in this room, and the energy has become murky. Moans of pain and growls of purge. People are falling apart all around me. There's a deep thud from across the room. Someone has fallen, close to the bathrooms. Shadows of Isabella and Charlie move towards the dark shape. A woman is moaning on the other side of the Maloka. It sounds like there's a demon inside her.

The darkness closes in.

*

Paulo closes the ceremony with his final song, and I sit in meditation. The others begin to crawl around the room and converse, but I still have work to do. I am used to this. I was prepared for this. There's no rush. The others congregate on the other side of the room, but I own my space, and I sit in quiet contemplation. The medicine shifts and there's a swelling in my belly. Deep nausea and cramping. I lie down and build to the purge that I know is coming. The medicine has been searching and it's finally found the knot, the demon, the block. The medicine has trapped the sickness, enveloped it, surrounded it, and now it's time to purge. It's time to get this shit out of me. I grasp my bucket and heave out my sickness. Again, I heave, and it gushes into the bucket. My stomach clenches and pulses and flings the sickness up out of me. Volumes of black liquid flows into my bucket. I splutter as I try to suck in air between the heaves.

Let it all out, brother.

And out it all comes.

I lie back onto my mat, exhausted. The others are gathered and talking, but I will lie on my mat a while longer.

The Maloka is lit by a few candles in the middle of the room. I sit up with my back against the wall. I take a mapacho and place it between my lips. I inhale the sweet smoke. I'm out of the woods. Isabella comes to my mat and sits with me.

'How are you feeling?' she asks.

'I'm out of the medicine. What was that crashing sound earlier on?'

'It was someone's first night. He shit himself on the way to the bathroom.'

'Heavy.'

'I had his poop on me.'

I laugh. 'That was a crazy ceremony. That woman on the other side of the Maloka. Is she okay?'

Isabella nods. 'She's fine. When you're ready, you should come and sit with me and Ellie.'

I gather my water bottle and mapachos and wander over to the girls.

'How was your night?' asks Ellie, sitting cross legged and holding hands with Isabella.

'I felt the energy in the room,' I say. 'More than I ever have before. And I felt the medicine more in my body. Not crazy visuals or anything, but more connected with the others in the Maloka, and within my own body.'

The girls smile and light fresh mapachos. I light one for myself.

'Before you came over to sit with us,' says Isabella, 'we were talking about destiny. Do you believe there is a path for everyone, Nicholas?'

'Here I was thinking you were talking about pancakes and pasta. Destiny… let me think. Well, I don't like the idea that my life is predetermined. I like to think that I have a choice in all this. If everything is already decided, then what's the point?'

'Destiny does not mean life is predetermined,' says Ellie. 'There is a path laid out for all of us, but it is up to us as individuals to identify our path, and to follow it.'

'So not everyone fulfils their destiny?' I ask.

'Most people don't even find their path,' says Isabella. 'They can get distracted along the way in their life.'

'But our higher self can help us to find our path,' says Ellie.

'How does ayahuasca fit into this?' I ask.

'For me,' says Isabella, 'drinking ayahuasca makes it easier to find my path. And it makes it harder to ignore my path. I still have much of my own work to do here. But I know that my

place is to help people who come to the centre. This is my path.'
She takes a draw from her mapacho and looks towards Ellie.

'And it was part of *my* destiny to be here,' says Ellie, 'so that I could meet Isabella, because we are soul-sisters!'

The girls hug each other.

'I like that,' I say. 'I've got a path, my destiny, and it's my purpose to find that path, and to follow it.'

'And if you don't find your path in this life,' says Ellie, 'then you try to find it in the next.'

'So, we can't escape our destiny, even after we are dead?' I say. 'That's a rather haunting prospect.'

'Our souls have a path,' says Ellie. 'With many lessons to learn, over many lifetimes.'

'Reincarnation,' I say. 'A convenient system for subjugation. It makes the lower classes much easier to dominate if they believe they'll be rewarded in the next life.'

'This is true,' says Isabella. 'But just because the system is easy to exploit by the elites, it doesn't mean that reincarnation doesn't exist. It could be that reincarnation exists *and* it is exploited by the elite class.'

'Maybe you are too cynical?' says Ellie. I think she's joking with me, but I can't be sure.

'Probably,' I say.

Ellie yawns and announces she is going back to her room to take a shower.

'Don't fall asleep,' says Isabella. 'I'm going to come to spoon you tonight.'

Isabella and I light another mapacho. The thought of Isabella spooning Ellie sends my mind on a ride. I take a sip of water to bring myself back to the Maloka. Not quite able to get my mind out of the bedroom, I ask Isabella why abstinence is recommended at the centre.

'Sex can deplete your energy. You need that sexual energy for more powerful and clearer ceremonies. But it's also very important with the *dietas* not to have sex, because when you are on diet, you are very open to energy.'

'So that's like, the tobacco diet?'

'Yes. You are still open for many days after you cut the diet. You can physically touch people, but you are so open that any kind of sexual contact can be dangerous. You can take on other people's energies very easily.'

'How long are you supposed to wait before you have sex?'

'Fourteen days,' she says. 'At least.' She can see I'm calculating in my head how many days there are between the last day of my tobacco diet and my arrival in Costa Rica. 'Perhaps you need to learn some self-control?'

I smile.

'And you should stick to the diet as well, Nick. No pork, no alcohol, no drugs.'

'That's going to be tough.'

'It's worth it. I know people who have stayed at Way of the Spirit that have had very bad experiences breaking the post-diet rules. You can become very sick.'

*

On my last morning at Way of the Spirit, I find time to visit with Tony and Charlie, and thank them for being such an important part of my experience.

Isabella and Ellie see me off on the banks of the river.

'Good luck with your travels,' says Ellie.

'Good luck working here.'

'You should come back sometime,' says Isabella.

'One day.'

I step onto the boat and wave to them both, then sombrely watch the riverbanks pass me by. In town it's heavy traffic and noise pollution. I take a key from the front desk at Hotel La Casona. My room smells of bleach, dust and air freshener. I sling my backpack onto a table, open it and hang a few clothes in the wardrobe. I take out my toiletries bag and leave it open in the bathroom. Then I slump onto the bed and burst into tears.

Part Three
The Holiday
August 2016

Chapter Sixteen
Getting to Costa Rica

I wait in the darkness on the wrong side of a barbed-wire fence with no way to tell if I'm at the right gate. There's a young couple standing next to a tree. The man holds a sleeping child to his chest. A trio of local men emerge from the shadows and stand a few feet away.

I check my boat ticket for the fourth time since the taxi dropped me off.

A local man wearing black trousers and a bomber jacket opens the gate from the inside, revealing another man who sits at a white plastic desk with a pen and clipboard. We file through and one by one report to the man at the desk. He checks my ticket then says something in Spanish that I don't catch, then gestures with his arm for me to walk towards the shore. Ahead, the ocean is black velvet, and the sky is heavy. There's no upper deck to the boat, just a single cabin with an aisle running down the centre. A few local fellows are onboard already, some asleep with their heads resting against the glass. I sit down towards the back with my daypack on the seat next to me and watch the people slowly filtering in. It takes forty-five minutes for the boat to eventually fill. I move my bag off a spare seat so a moustachioed man can sit down, and plug in my headphones as the boat putters away from the shore. The engine is terribly loud, the cabin is crowded, and it stinks of body sweat and chicken grease. I can't see beyond the first line of trees at the river's bank, and it doesn't take long before I surrender all fantasies of a romantic traipse along the Amazon River and accept that this voyage will be more like a bus trip than a river cruise.

I spent most of yesterday crying into my pillow at Hotel La Casona.

It's alright, I'm not miserable anymore. Just empty. It feels like I've been stabbed in the guts with a bayonet, and it's being slowly turned, and while the blade is turning, my spirit is oozing out of the wound. What I wouldn't give to be sharing a mapacho with Ellie and Isabella.

When we arrive at the port in Santa Rosa, some seven hours later, I share a taxi with a gringo couple who have the same plan as me: an exit stamp in Santa Rosa, a taxi-boat to Leticia, a taxi to the airport to get an entry stamp for Colombia, and then a taxi back into town.

Santa Rosa Immigration is nothing more than a demountable propped up in a mud patch. The immigration officer says, via a mixture of gestures and Spanish, something along the lines of: 'The system is down, gringos. Come back tomorrow.'

'We can try the police,' says my male gringo friend after a brief discussion with our taxi driver. I wipe the sweat from my forehead and find I have a layer of boat-filth and river grime on my skin. A few demountables down the road is the Police

Station, where a lone Peruvian man sits on a swivel chair with his feet up on the desk and his hands clasped behind his head. The man's hair is black and slick, and his upper lip hidden behind a moustache. The top three buttons of his shirt are undone, and his underarms are heavy with sweat. When my gringo companion enquires about our migration situation, the police officer strokes his moustache a few times, then says something along the lines of this: 'We don't have the right computer system, gringos. Go back to immigration tomorrow.'

Great. Now what?

'We should look for somewhere to stay in Leticia,' says the gringo, more to his girlfriend than to me. 'It's probably nicer than here.'

She agrees.

'I've already got a room booked over there,' I say. 'But how can we go without a passport stamp?'

'We can come back to Santa Rosa tomorrow morning. The policeman said we have twenty-four hours to get stamped.'

It stinks of petrol and fish guts down by the riverbank where young men wait to ferry travellers across to the Colombian or Brazilian borders. The gringos and I hop into one of the little motorised canoes for the ten-minute trip to Leticia. At the Colombian banks, the driver opens his bumbag to reveal wads of cash. I pay for the ride with Peruvian soles and receive a mix of Brazilian reals and Colombian pesos for change. When I look at him quizzically, he grins. *Don't worry about it, gringo.*

I part ways with the couple. I have to stop to ask a few people for directions on the way to my hotel, but eventually find it without too much fuss. After checking-in, I drop my bags in my room and race to the toilet.

It's the goddamn tap arse.

I need tap arse like I need a broken leg.

In the early evening, I walk to a restaurant recommended by the lady at the front desk of my hotel. The air is warm, and the streets are green and clean. There are children roaming freely, kicking soccer balls in the fading light. Leticia appears to be Santa Rosa's well-to-do cousin.

I take my dinner silently, watching the locals wander in and out. I smoke a mapacho on the walk home. When I lie down in bed, I feel faint and weak, and a little like I'm not a part of my body.

I wake up drenched in sweat with a terrible headache after a restless and tormenting night of erotic fever dreams. Ellie came to me in my sleep, but so did many ghouls and spiders.

*

Having done the back and forth to both borders and successfully sorted out my immigration without shitting myself in public, I sit at the front porch of the hotel in the afternoon, savouring a mapacho and contemplating my path to Costa Rica. First will be a flight from Leticia to Bogota, flying over the Colombian Amazon. Then a connecting flight from Bogota to Panama City. From there I'll fly to San José, capital of Costa Rica. Then a short plane ride to the beach town of Tamarindo. I still need to book a flight out of Costa Rica – Craig is keen on a boat trip from Panama to Colombia – so when I've finished my mapacho, I move inside to the computers and stay up most of the night trying to book a flight to Panama City.

When I'm finally alone in the darkness of my bedroom, Ellie comes to me again.

The following morning, desire overwhelms me, and I masturbate in a pool of my own sweat and sickness. It's my first orgasm in three weeks, and it's wonderful. But soon after I'm left drained of all life-force, feeling something like a hollowed-out egg.

*

At the Leticia Airport check-in desk, the officers want proof of exit from Costa Rica, and I thank my stars I stayed up late booking a ticket to Panama. But then the lady asks me for proof of exit from Panama.

'*Por que?*' I say. '*Yo tengo* proof of exit from Costa Rica. I'm travelling by boat, ahh… *viajar en barco* from Panama to Colombia. *No reservado mi boleto.* I can't buy a ticket to Colombia yet because I have to inspect the boat first. I can't book *el barco* until I get to Panama. *Cuál es el problemo?*'

There's much discussion behind the counter.

'I can show you *mi avion boleto* from Peru to Australia. Would that help?' I hand over a printout of my ticket. 'This is for when I return home. *Para el retorno.*'

The lady nods her head and smiles.

'*Es bien?*' I ask.

'*Si.*'

Fucking bien.

*

Yesterday was my flight from Leticia to Bogota. I had a layover for a few hours before my flight to Panama. I arrived here in Panama around midnight facing a nine-hour wait until my flight to San José. I spent the first hour in the bathroom with tap arse and now I'm wandering through the airport looking for the best floorspace to sleep. I settle on a patch of carpet under a set of hard plastic seats and roll my rain jacket into a pillow. I slip a padlock through the zipper on my daypack and sling my arm through one of the shoulder straps to prevent anyone running off with it. My headphones drown out the airport announcements and I manage to scrape together a few scattered hours of sleep before my alarm goes off. I sit up bleary-eyed and hazy-brained. There's still plenty of time until boarding, so I wander off to charge my phone at a power point on a wall. When I've got enough juice to last me the flight, I drift closer to the departure gate. Ten minutes until boarding and no-one is lining up yet. I guess they'll make an announcement soon, or else, I'm sure that all these people around me will start moving when it's time to board. I scroll through my phone. I flick through songs. I turn to face the desk. No-one is lining up. I check my phone. I check my ticket. I check my phone again. My plane's supposed to have left by now. How is that possible? I feel a slow, creeping dread. Shallow breaths. I rise from my chair and sling my daypack over one shoulder. At the desk, my voice seems to be coming from a small child rather than a man. '*Ahh, hola. Es plane to San José?*'

'That plane left fifteen minutes ago,' says a young, uniformed man with sculpted black hair. 'We were here. You were not here.'

The little child in me wants to cry. 'But I was just over there,' I say pointing to my seat. 'I didn't hear the boarding call, I –'

'We called for you, but you were not here. I am sorry but the plane has already left.'

This is one of those sinking feelings they talk about. It's a cliché, but I don't know how else to describe it. The whole world around me has become silent. It's just me and the young, uniformed man with sculpted black hair and that smug look on his face. I don't have the energy to fight.

'What can I do now?'

'You have to go downstairs to baggage pick-up,' he says. 'Go to carousel number five and get your bag, go through immigration, then go to the Avianca desk to buy another ticket. You must pay the fee and the fare difference. There is another flight at four o'clock, but I don't know if this flight is full or not. The office doesn't open until two.'

I'll miss my connecting flight from San José to Tamarindo. All that careful planning. All those trips into Iquitos, all for nothing. And of course, the money down the drain. I could've survived two weeks out here on that plane ticket.

Down the stairs towards immigration. I want to smash something to pieces. I want to rip my jacket apart. I want to rip that beautifully sculpted hair from that young uniformed man's head. I want to pull the flesh from someone's face off. My anger and frustration turn inwards, and I want to cry, and I want to rip the flesh from my own face. In the lines to immigration, tracks of little tears escape down my cheeks. I want to cry all over the lady at the desk.

Fuck! If only I could turn back the clock twenty minutes. That's all it would take!

After immigration, I walk to the carousel to collect my bag. I hurry to the Avianca desk and, as Officer Smugface said, it's not open yet. I sit on the floor for a moment and cry as quietly as possible.

Jesus, what's wrong with me? I can't even cope with a goddamn airport. There are too many people in here. The pulsing neon lights. I can't handle this shit. I hate every single person in here. I am fucking hopeless. Why can't this just be easy? How did I let this happen? Why am I so fucking fragile?

I sit for ten minutes of self-loathing outside Avianca, trying to connect to the internet on my phone before I move upstairs in search of stronger WIFI. I can't find Avianca's four o'clock flight to San José online but there's a flight on the website leaving at ten-thirty tonight. The ticket costs five hundred dollars, so I'll have to pay a couple of hundred bucks to make up for the more expensive flight, and I'll need to pay the change fee of seventy dollars as well.

And it'll mean another twelve-hour wait…

Just get on the later flight, dude. It's no big deal. Go back and sleep on the floor somewhere. You'll be fine.

No! I can't! I literally can't do it. I'm suffocating in this airport already. I can't sleep on the floor again. I have to get the fuck out of here or I'm gonna lose my mind.

Another option presents itself in the form of the blinking lights of the Copa Airlines sign. I jog over to the Copa ticket office where an overweight and empathetic woman serves me. She can squeeze me onto a flight leaving in two hours for three hundred dollars.

After hesitating, stepping away from the desk to think for five minutes, I step back and ask her to put through the purchase. My Citibank card doesn't work, and the butterflies in my guts spin themselves up into a frenzy.

Calm down Nick, Jesus!

I try my Bankwest card and it works. I buy the fucking ticket, hand over my backpack, then walk upstairs. The bayonet in my belly slowly turns again, like it's hooked up to a spit-roaster.

At a café with strong WIFI, I call Craig and explain the situation. He just laughs and then he recommends a hostel to stay at in San José.

And then I wonder if perhaps I've been overreacting.

I need a holiday from my goddamn mind.

Chapter Seventeen
Tamarindo

My bus arrives in Tamarindo in the late afternoon, and I find my way to the bar on the beach where Craig said he and his mate Glassy would meet me when they've finished their boat trip. I would've been on that trip had I not missed my goddamn flight.

…I've let all that go now.

Yesterday, when I eventually got into San José, I smoked a few mapachos in the hostel courtyard and made friends with some travellers. I decided to book a bus to Tamarindo rather than fork out for another flight, and then I treated myself to a seafood dinner.

I leave my bags at the front desk of the bar and take a seat at a table on the beach. Two gorgeous women in bikinis walk side by side across the beach, their feet kissing the water, their hair falling back down behind them. I kick off my shoes and socks and drive my feet into the sand. The mist from the ocean floats over and cleanses me. It's warm enough outside that I could easily slip off my shirt and be comfortable, but not so hot that I feel I must. I order a beer and make a cheers to myself.

Here's to a new chapter, Nicholas old boy, and the end to a stupid fucking week.

The boats begin to sail into shore as the sun gently dips to touch the horizon. There's a little tension still in my belly, but for the first time since Way of the Spirit, I'm starting to relax. The bayonet has been removed, there's just some tender scar tissue left behind.

I catch a glimpse of Craig and Glassy approaching from a hundred metres away. They are shirtless and animated. Glassy's a little taller than Craig, and better fed as well.

'Hey friend!' says Craig, as he wraps me up in a hug. Craig's skin is well-tanned, his hair longer, and his face a few weeks unshaven.

'Nicko,' says Glassy, holding out his hand and shaking mine, 'Good to meet ya mate, how were your flights?' Glassy's got a buzz-cut and a dirty little moustache.

'Great to meet you, Glassy. Don't ask about the flights. How's it going here?'

'Just another day in paradise,' says Craig.

'*Tres cervezas, por favor,*' says Glassy holding out three fingers to a passing waiter, and then he lights a dart, takes a seat and explains to me that he and Craig dropped acid a few hours ago and reality is starting to get a bit difficult to manage. 'Old mate from around these parts,' he says taking a drag from his cigarette, 'fucken said he was getting us MDMA.' He chuckles and looks at Craig. Craig laughs and drives his hand through his curly mop of hair.

'So how was the boat ride?' I ask.

'Pretty good overall,' says Craig. 'All things considered. We were expecting a few more hotties on the boat, to be honest. There were just a few local dudes, a couple of Swedes, and this American family with teenage kids.'

'The daughter was alright,' says Glassy.

'*Mate*,' says Craig before dragging a cold beer out of the bucket that's just been placed down. Glassy and I each grab a beer and then we cheers.

'Welcome to Tamarindo, Nicko,' says Craig.

'Great to be here, boys,' I say. 'Thanks for inviting me.'

'We'll try not to make this evening too weird for ya,' says Glassy, 'but you know, no promises.' He makes this kind of chuckling sound and Craig lets a suppressed laugh burst out. I take a long drink from my beer.

The sun dips down below the sea, and the sky turns dark and begins to sprinkle with rain. We pay the bill, and I collect my bags from behind the bar. The boys are still shirtless, their clothes in the bag on Craig's back. We walk to a local store to pick up beer, vodka, avocados and bananas, then press on to the Airbnb.

The apartment complex is an aesthetic marriage between Native American adobe pueblos and Florida Beach condos. Glassy's been staying at the apartment for almost two weeks. His wife was with him at first but recently flew home to work. Craig drifted down from Mexico shortly after she left. There's a locked gate to get through, then a pool and outdoor shower. Up a flight of stairs and around a corner and we are at the front door. Inside, the air conditioner has been working in our absence.

'Fuck yeah, that's a good temp,' says Glassy, as he moves towards the fridge to load the beers. There are two couches to the left of the entrance, with a laptop on the coffee table. The kitchen and bathroom are straight ahead. To the right is a set of stairs and below them is a round wooden table. The first thing I notice on the table is the enormous pile of loose change. The second thing I notice is the enormous pile of cocaine.

I sit on the couch by the front door, and Craig and Glassy sit opposite me. They've each shifted twice already to take a line at the dinner table. Glassy invites me to dive in but I politely decline.

'No thanks boys. Gotta stay off the drugs. It's the post-diet rules.' I give the boys the headlines of my time in the jungle and promise to tell them more about it later. 'I don't really feel like going down that rabbit hole just yet. Tell me more about the boat trip? Did you scare the American family?'

'We didn't really know how hard we could ramp it with the Americans there,' says Craig. 'We convinced the dad to have a coupla beers. And the son as well, though the mum seemed pretty pissed off with that.'

'The dad didn't appreciate you cracking onto his daughter the whole time either.'

'Stop it,' says Craig.

A little later, we decide to walk into town.

'We'll just go for a look,' says Glassy, lighting a cigarette as we hit the road. He passes the lighter to Craig who lights a cigarette, then he to me, and I light one of my mapachos.

'What's going on with that big old thing in your mouth?' asks Craig.

'It's jungle tobacco. They grow it down in Iquitos. You can buy these pre-rolled in the markets. I bought a whole brick at the markets before I left Iquitos.'

I pass the mapacho to Craig. He inhales, splutters and hands it back to me.

'Jesus mate, are you sure you're supposed to inhale that shit?'

'Takes a bit of getting used to,' I say. 'I don't even smoke back home. But I developed a taste for these at the centre. I started out using it in ceremonies to mask the taste of the ayahuasca, but eventually it became something to do during the day instead of drinking coffee or beers. It's kinda like being at rehab.'

'I don't smoke back home either,' says Craig as he takes a drag of his cigarette.

'You boys are fucken idiots,' says Glassy. 'Don't go and get yourself addicted like me.'

We turn a corner and make our way in the direction of the beach. At the bar, Glassy buys a round of beers and we perch outside close to the DJ booth. There's about twenty people outside and the same inside. Most are sweaty tourists in beach clothes. A man with a fedora hat starts chatting up a girl about ten yards in front of us.

'I was wearing one of those for a couple of weeks in Mexico,' says Craig.

'A fedora?' asks Glassy.

Craig nods.

'It's a tough look to pull off,' I say. 'Unless you're in a ska band.'

Glassy snorts. 'That was savage, Nicko.'

We go for a walk into the parking lot so the boys can top up on coke.

'How's it going with the ladies, Craig?' I ask.

'Honestly,' he says, before pausing to either consider his words or to create a dramatic effect. 'Pretty good.'

'I've been enjoying it,' says Glassy. 'I've been living vicariously through Craig's cock.'

'Hooked up with the hottest chick the other night,' says Craig. 'Like genuinely, the most gorgeous girl that I've ever been with. She works at a café here. I've been seriously thinking about applying for a visa.'

'Are you on the pull, Nicko?' asks Glassy.

I hesitate for a few moments, not sure how to approach my reply. 'I'm having a go at abstinence,' I say. 'Started in the jungle.' I half-expected one of the boys to shout, *'Gay!'* but they seem to get where I'm coming from.

Craig says, 'I actually did that when I was about eighteen. I thought at the time that sex ruins all relationships. I was abstinent for about a year.'

'I was abstinent when I was eighteen as well,' says Glassy, 'but that's just 'cos I couldn't get laid.'

*

When I wake up, Craig's not in his bed. I only had a few beers last night but still my head is thumping, and my mouth is dry. I take a cold shower then slowly make my way down to the kitchen. Craig hands me a steaming mug of instant coffee.

'Legend,' I say.

'Have some guacamole mate, just made a fresh batch.'

I take my breakfast onto the balcony, overlooking the quiet neighbourhood, and when I've finished eating, enjoy a mapacho with the sun on my face.

Later in the morning, the three of us stroll down to the beach for a swim. Glassy orders a round of beers at a bar and we make ourselves comfortable, perving on some gorgeous tourists at one of the adjacent bars.

'It's a tough life,' says Craig. He looks over to the girls and laughs, shaking his head. Glassy lights a dart then quickly pulls out his phone.

'Fuck,' he says. 'There's never a moment's rest over here.'

'What's going on?' I ask.

'Local drug dealers hounding me.'

Shit. 'You owe them money?'

'Nah, man. Old mate's trying to sell me more drugs. They're really pushy over here. Always texting me saying they've got new shit just in, trying to give me free samples.'

'This is in contrast,' says Craig, 'to back home where drug dealers are the flakiest fucking guys around. You've gotta think in advance because they're liable to skip town. You've gotta call at specific times of the day or they won't pick up.'

'Old mate's saying he's just got some new shit in from Peru that's the best shit he's ever got. He wants me to try it. I just don't know how to say no to this guy.' Glassy lets out a sigh and takes a drag from his cigarette. 'It's a tough life indeed.'

I'm distracted by an argument taking place at the next bar over. A well-tanned but overweight shirtless man is in a heated discussion with a bartender. They're speaking Spanish, so I can't tell what it's about. The shirtless man throws his hands up in the air then stumbles over towards our bar. He stops to piss against a tree. I turn to look at the gorgeous tourists. I turn back to see the shirtless man approaching our table.

'What's up, faggots?' he says, as he walks past our table, knocking an empty beer bottle onto the sand. 'You gringos are so *white*.'

And then he walks off down the beach.

'Wow,' says Glassy. 'Savage.'

*

Life in Tamarindo slips into a groove. I wake up whenever I feel like it, drink coffee, eat guacamole and smoke mapacho. The three of us go for a swim in the afternoon, and in the evening, Craig and Glassy decide whether they're going to dive into a pile of cocaine or just chill-out at a bar and have a few drinks.

Most nights, Ellie comes to me in my dreams.

This particular afternoon, we're back at the Airbnb after a swim. Craig puts on a load of washing then starts mixing up a batch of guacamole. I write some notes in my journal and Glassy announces he's off to the ATM.

'Gonna withdraw a million dollars for drugs,' he says.

I take a seat on the couch, and Craig hands me a cold beer and a bowl of guacamole. After a few moments of silent eating and drinking, I ask Craig if he knows what he's going to do with himself when he gets back home, and he makes this 'ugh' sound of disgust.

'*If* I go back home, mate,' he says. '*If* I go home. And the answer is *fuck knows*. Why, have you got it all figured out yet?'

'I've got a few options. I've thought about moving back to Melbourne. But if I do go back to Perth, I could probably get a job teaching at the same school I left earlier this year.'

'Do you even *like* teaching, though?'

'There's a lot I love about it. Young people have this natural energy and curiosity that's infectious. And teaching is really stimulating work. I have to take these difficult concepts, fully understand them, then figure out a way to explain them to thirty different brains at once. I gotta think on my feet to come up with some analogy to their lives that'll make it all make sense.

'But it's also soul destroying. Because I have to do that for five classes at once. So that's like a hundred and fifty kids. And

I do it, because, like the fucking chump that I am, I actually give a shit about these kids and can't just phone it in. And then there's the endless piles of essays to mark. And planning for the next term during school break, when everyone thinks I'm kicking back on holiday. Not to mention goddamn upper management. Making us go to endless, repetitive, useless fucking professional development seminars whenever one of them is doing their PhD and wants to use us as their subject matter, instead of giving us the one thing we need – time to prepare for our fucking classes. These days there's a big drive on collecting quantitative data; everything has to be meticulously recorded on multiple online platforms. Again, all of this happens in the time when I could be marking my endless pile of essays, or preparing for the class I'm about to deliver. Christ almighty! *How do we achieve better educational outcomes?* Management asks rhetorically. Well, how about we start by reducing class sizes, and reducing the number of classes teachers have to teach. Then teachers would actually have the time and space to cater for individual student needs.'

'Why don't they just do that then?'

'Because education is a business. Reducing class sizes and lowering teacher loads would be too expensive. And teachers, being compassionate individuals, are willing to kill themselves to do this stupid fucking job. I dunno man. Sometimes I think it's all wrong. Like, the whole system.'

'What's wrong with the system?'

'Nothing's wrong with the system if what we want is anxious, compliant adults addicted to social media, caffeine and anti-depressants who can follow orders, memorise information, seek external validation and approval, and operate in hierarchies. If that's what we want, then the school system works perfectly. If we want creative people, free thinking, critical, intelligent, empowered, emotionally developed, socially developed, compassionate adults then we have to make some changes.'

'What would you do to change the system?'

'What the fuck would I know, man? I'm just a confused, frustrated cog in the machine. When it comes down to it, I think it's wrong to force kids to be in a classroom when they just want to run around and play outside. I don't think it's healthy for kids to be held inside all day.'

'Same with adults,' says Craig.

'It's not what human beings are supposed to be doing, right? Like, with our time here on Earth. How did we fuck this up so bad?'

Craig and I each take a contemplative swig from our beers.

'The answer for me might be just getting out of the city,' I say. 'Why try to fight the system when I can just move out to the countryside, live in an alternative community, and grow organic snow peas and marijuana?'

'Why the hell not?' Craig finishes the rest of his beer. 'You want another one?' he asks, taking our empty bowls up to the kitchen.

'Yeah mate,' I say, tipping the rest of my beer down my throat.

Craig returns with a couple of fresh beers. 'Are you gonna look for a different job, then. Get out of teaching?'

'I don't know what else I could do.'

Craig stares into space for a while then says, 'Alright then. Let me lay an idea on ya. What if you look at it this way? You're a writer, aren't you? That's what you told me in Peru. *That's* your passion.'

'I'm a *failed* writer.'

'Jesus mate! Listen to yourself. A *failed* writer! So, your book's been rejected a few times.'

'Seven.'

'That's nothing, mate. Everyone gets rejected. Seven times at least, mate. Usually eight times. Everyone gets rejected. Successful writers are just the ones who didn't give up.'

'You're right.'

'Of course I'm right. Okay, so you're a writer.' He looks at me with raised eyebrows and I nod to keep him going. 'That's your passion, that's your purpose. So, what if you treat teaching just as a job. That's just something you do to make money. And that way you can stop putting all this pressure onto teaching to be something that it's not. Can you accept it for what it is, and just say *fuck it* to all the bullshit that goes along with it? 'Cos every job comes with a load of bullshit, trust me mate, I've worked a million of them.'

'Treat it as a job.'

'It's just a job. It's just how you pay the bills. And then write your books on the side. And that shit's what makes you happy.'

*

Craig and I take down a few more beers and then sink into our respective couches and just as I'm nodding off, I think about the end of my last school year. Kids love the end of the year, of course, but it's a special time for teachers as well. We spend the whole year keeping our heads above water, staying one lesson ahead of the kids, absorbing all the anxiety and tension, fighting off colds and the flu, until the end of the year when we can finally let go. That's why school Christmas parties are the best. After a whole year of repression, teachers get one day to let it all out. At last year's Christmas party, I hooked up with

199

one of the primary school staff members in what ended up being a rather public display of affection, but that's neither here nor there.

There's a tradition in some schools of students giving presents to their teachers. Usually, it's chocolates or flowers, but sometimes, the kids come out with something thoughtful. And it's moments like these, right at the end of the year, at the last possible moment, that a teacher feels appreciated, almost enough to seriously consider doing it all over again.

Last year, a girl from my Year 7 class gave me a plastic golden apple and a card with a Fibonacci spiral shell on the front. Inside the card she'd written: *A golden apple for a golden teacher*. During the year we'd studied ancient Greek and Roman mythology, and I told the story of the Judgement of Paris & the Golden Apple of Discord. This was my way of subtly exposing the kids to the Goddess Eris and Discordianism. I'm not sure if the girl understood how symbolic her gift was. It doesn't really matter because *I* got the message.

Another gift came from Amelia. She was in my Year 10 English class. Amelia didn't fit in well with the other students. She would get bullied for not wearing the latest fashion trends. She used to send me poetry during the week, and in class we'd work on it together while the other students listened to music and played games and threw scrunched up pieces of paper at each other. Amelia gave me a handmade felt coaster embroidered with the faces of John, Paul, George and Ringo.

But the most beautiful gift came from one of my Year 12 English students. Her name was Asha. I'd worked overtime with this girl throughout the year. Her mother was in the school English Department as well, and we used to discuss her progress at length. Anyway, Asha knocked on the staffroom door one afternoon late last year. When I appeared, she thanked me for helping her and handed me a gorgeously written card with a small, wrapped package. Her gift was a framed picture of a church, with the inscription: *Firenze Santa Croce*. In her English class that year we'd studied *A Room with a View*. The novel took me two reads to appreciate. During the first read, I was bored shitless and wondered how the hell I'd sell this old Edwardian novel as a good idea to the kids. But on the second read through something clicked, and I began to notice nuances, and the subtle way Forster manipulated language. Even though I'd never *choose* to read that novel, I could still dig down into the text and appreciate its beauty. I realised then that it was my job to help my students develop those same skills that would allow them to appreciate a piece of art. It was my job to help them gain access to messages hidden within language, that otherwise, they would miss. Some of them, of course, couldn't give a shit, but for others, like Asha, it makes a difference to their lives. See, when Asha was on the school trip to Italy last year, and visited the Santa Croce Church – the very church that features in *A Room with a View* – she bought a little framed picture for me at the end of their tour.

I let the thoughtfulness of this gift sink in, with Asha blushing in front of me. Instead of falling to bits and crying, I opened my arms, gave her a hug and thanked her. Back at my desk, my old mate Jim Swanson handed me the last beer we'd share together, and I placed the framed picture of the Santa Croce Church next to my plastic golden apple, and an unsigned copy of a teaching contract for the following year.

*

Craig and I are napping in the living room when Glassy bursts through the front door.

'I've got something to wake you cunts up,' he says, tossing an enormous bag of cocaine onto the kitchen table. 'Suck on that carton of nose beers.'

The boys take down a few lines each, Glassy throws on some Pink Floyd, and pleasant little butterflies start to flap their wings inside my belly.

'You know what,' I say, 'I might just dive in and have a line, hey?'

'Go for it, mate,' says Glassy.

I regard the great mountain of drugs in front of me. Glassy's arranged half a dozen lines already, so I have merely to roll up the Australian fifty dollar note, place one end into my nostril, block the other nostril with my left thumb and inhale deeply. I swap my thumb and nostril and repeat on the other side. *It's not unlike pranayama breathwork…*

I settle back down on the couch. Craig has made vodka sodas, and he passes them around. David Gilmour's guitar soars. My heart rate kicks in. For some strange reason I suddenly feel very excited…

'I knew you'd be into it,' says Glassy letting out a wide grin.

'Yeah look,' I say, 'I wasn't sure whether the coke would mix well with my system or not. But then I thought, fuck it.'

'We were wondering how long it would take,' says Craig. 'I actually thought you'd hold out longer.'

We take down the lion's share of a bottle of vodka and a few beers each, with regular trips to the kitchen table to top up on white powder. I tune out from the conversation for a while to check in with my body. I feel a little bit sick in my stomach but also a little bit like a fucking millionaire. I tune back in and Craig says, 'I think along the same lines…' though I'm not sure of the context of what he's saying. 'I've thought a lot lately about my relationship with my ex. I sometimes wonder if I could've done things differently. If we'd broken up earlier, would I have been happier? Could we have made it work if we both acted differently? But I figure that all that stuff made me who I am today. Even the shit stuff helped me grow.'

'I gotta say Craig,' says Glassy. 'And I know I've said it before, and I know that you won't mind me saying this with Nicko here, but it's good to have you back, mate.'

'What do you mean by that?' I ask.

'I was tellin' Craig a little while back that since him and his ex broke up, Craig's become a way better bloke. He used to be this fun guy back when we were younger, and then, well, no offence Craig but you became a bit of a boring, button-up shirt wearing fuck. And I know we've talked about this before, but yeah, it's just fucken great to see you happy and being a funny bastard again. It's great just having you back in my life again.'

'Aw mate,' says Craig, and they slap hands in one of those tennis player handshakes. I take this beautiful and intimate moment to slip up to the fridge to collect three more beers and slip a line into my brain on the way back.

Chapter Eighteen
The Calling

Glassy went too hard last night and is still passed the fuck out in his room so it's just me and Craig out tonight looking for the right vibe. We approach a timeworn tapas bar with a cluster of attractive, young Latinos drinking cocktails and smoking cigarettes on the front porch. Through the front door are couples drinking red wine and sharing plates of roasted meats and bread. In the back courtyard a band plays the blues for locals who dance and smoke. Craig and I double back to the bar then return to the courtyard with beers. Amongst the locals dancing to the band are a pair of tourists. The man has his arm around the woman's waist while she videos the band on her phone. I chin-nod towards the pair and mutter to Craig, 'What's with the filming? How about you just enjoy the band?'

'Gotta capture this precious moment, bro.'

'This kinda thing gets to me,' I say. 'Taking a video of a band takes you out of the present moment and basically guarantees that you'll never actually experience the band.'

'How so?'

'While you're taking the video, *that's* what you're focussed on. And at home, if you ever actually watch the video, you're not watching the band live, you're watching a video of the band. You could've watched them on YouTube. A video of a band will never compare to what it feels like to watch a band live. But you'll never realise that because you weren't watching the band in the first place.'

'You got it all wrong, dude. They're not gonna watch it later, that video is going straight up on Insta. Hashtag local band. Hashtag authentic experience. That kinda thing.'

'Jesus. I forgot about social media.'

'It's about the validation you get from the interaction on social media. People commenting on your video like, *Oh, cool bro, you're at that cool band, you must be so cool.*'

I take a long drink from my beer. 'Do you reckon posting something online cheapens the experience? My mates just posted a bunch of photos from the Inca Trail and Machu Picchu, and even a few from Way of the Spirit. I don't know how I feel about it.'

'What's the problem?'

'Does it detract from the experience?'

'People want to see what you're up to, man. Don't think about it so much.'

'But what if it was like, a spiritual experience? Like for me, Machu Picchu was a spiritual experience. Does posting photos online cheapen it?'

'Not necessarily. I think it's got to do with the intention. If you go to Machu Picchu and spend the whole day walking around soaking it in, taking a few pics here and there, and then later that day post some of the photos, I reckon that's all good. But if you're live streaming or tweeting or whatever from Machu Picchu, I'd say that crosses the line. Also hash tagging,

I'd say that's a good indicator. Hashtag so blessed. Hashtag so connected. Hashtag so grateful. That kinda shit.'

'Hashtag so fingered.'

'I'd say that for any important experience to really soak in, you need a little time to process it.'

We both take long gulps from our beers.

'Hold on,' I say, 'what if it's not actually the *experience* itself that's important for these people. What if it's the *feeling* they get from being able to *say* that they've had the experience, that's the important bit.'

'Don't follow.'

'What if it's the feeling that comes from being publicly witnessed, via social media, as having a particular kind of experience – like, a *hashtag spiritual experience* – that brings on an endorphin rush from all the 'likes', that becomes, in effect, the *source* of the spiritual experience? The social media experience *is* the spiritual experience.'

'If no-one likes your Insta post about your spiritual awakening at the yoga retreat, then are you really hashtag enlightened?'

'Exactly.'

We pause to light cigarettes.

'Having said that, though,' I say, exhaling a cloud of mapacho smoke, 'we are both in the process of writing books. Are we not also seeking approval from others to legitimise or validate our own experiences?'

'No,' says Craig, after contemplating the question for a moment. 'It's definitely different. And I'm not just saying that so that we can feel better about ourselves. Well, maybe a little bit. But I think the time we're taking to process and reflect on our experiences is significant. It's the effort to construct a narrative and to labour over the arguments and points that we're making.'

'So rather than rushing to post something online straight away,' I say, 'by taking the time to reflect and to construct an extended piece of work, we can draw greater meaning from the experience and convey it to others as a piece of art, rather than a grab for attention.'

'Yeah. Well, whatever we need to sleep at night.'

*

Lying in bed on the last morning in Tamarindo, I'm seriously considering a return to Way of the Spirit. Ellie came to me in another dream last night, but this time it was different. This dream was the most lucid of all of them. She appeared to me as a shining golden Goddess in a shimmering white dress. I told her I was in love with her, and she replied: 'No you're not.' I was taken aback. She said, 'You're projecting love onto me. You're in love with the idea of me. It's your own inner feminine you're seeking a relationship with.' When she vanished, I didn't feel rejected, I felt accepted and at peace.

The idea of returning to the Centre has been creeping around in the back of my mind for some time. Certainly, while I was falling apart in my hotel room in Iquitos, I thought about catching the next canoe straight back to Way of the Spirit, but I figured it was just the shock of leaving the nest and that I should harden the fuck up because it would get better. I assumed that was *it* as far as my journey with ayahuasca was concerned. It never occurred to me that my journey might just be beginning.

The money, though. That'll be the end of my savings. I'll have to find a job as soon as I get back to Perth.

Oh God, the horror…

*

For our last night in Tamarindo we decide just to hang out at the Airbnb and smoke cigarettes, drink red wine and snort cocaine. Craig tells stories about Mexico, Glassy tells stories about working FIFO, and I tell stories about drinking ayahuasca.

'There was this Realm I'd go to,' I say, shuffling around on the red-tiled floor of the balcony. 'It's like this alien realm of colour and light, where everything melts into everything else. It's hard to describe just how intense the whole thing is. It's not even that it's scary or joyful, it's just *intense*. I think that's probably the one thing I really wasn't prepared for. Everyone talks about the visions but what I found most alarming was the *intensity* of the experience. That's the thing you can't replicate with words, or on a screen. I'd get this overwhelming sensation that something profound was happening. Sometimes I'd be just breathing, but it was as though I was breathing for the first time in my life. In those moments, existence really was a matter of life and death.'

'Do you reckon it's dangerous?' asks Craig.

'It depends how you look at it,' I say. 'I've heard of cowboy ayahuasceros out there, who *are* dangerous. Because you're in such a vulnerable state you can be manipulated. But if you find a good shaman then I guess it's safe. You might *feel* like you're dying. Or you might *feel* like you're going insane. That was my fear. I was afraid of becoming stuck in that world, and not being able to return from a trip, like the kids at the top of the Magic Faraway Tree.' The boys don't get my reference… 'I think it's more dangerous to live your life *without* the experience of

208

ayahuasca. You could go your whole life thinking *this*,' I say pointing around the balcony, 'is reality. Or at least, that *this* is the *only* reality. Ayahuasca is dangerous if you want to continue to live the same way you've always lived. To look at the world the same way you always have. If you want to keep your worldview, then ayahuasca is really dangerous.'

'How did yours change, then?' asks Glassy.

'Reality is balanced on a knife's edge. My reality, my identity, everything that I am, is balanced on a knife's edge. Everything I take for granted in daily life. Everything about me can be taken away in a second. And then what's left? That's the real question.'

A sense of knowing washes over me.

When a decision like this is made, it's so obvious we wonder how it didn't occur to us earlier. My story will not end here. There are too many unanswered questions. I have unfinished business at Way of the Spirit. I have to return to the jungle.

'I think I'm spent guys,' I say, and take myself off to bed via the toilet for a cocaine-induced anxiety shit.

*

Subject: Return to Way of the Spirit?

Hi Isabella, how are you?

I miss you and the whole crew at Way of the Spirit so much! I'm so grateful that we had the opportunity to connect. Thank you for all your help.

It's a bit embarrassing but straight after leaving, when I checked into my hotel in Iquitos, I lay on my bed and cried. I felt so vulnerable being alone in the city rather than in our community in the jungle. It was much harder than I thought it'd be.

My time at Way of the Spirit was probably the most powerful experience of my life, and though there were some hard times, it was also one of the happiest and funniest times I've had for a while.

I thought I had things all figured out for the rest of my time in South America, and going back to Australia, but now I'm unsure again. So, I guess what I'm leading to is this… I'd love to come back to Way of the Spirit. Do you have any space available during September? Or even late August? Let me know.

Oh, and can you please say hi to Ellie for me?

Much love

Nick

Xo

Chapter Nineteen
Medellin, Colombia

Craig and I sit quietly in the back seat of a cab on the way from the airport to our hostel in Medellin. Craig's let his beard grow out, but underneath his skin is pale and his lips are cracked and blistered. I rest my head on the car window. The cloudy, drizzling sky and the rolling, hilly countryside, thick with forest and grass, provides a stark contrast to the beaches and shrubs of northern Colombia...

After Tamarindo, Glassy flew back home to Sydney, and Craig and I caught a plane down to Panama, where we spent four glorious days cruising around the San Blas Islands. Our home island was the size of a football field, and the ground was spongey sand, almost like soggy astro-turf. The accommodation was nothing more than a series of one room shacks, built out of light wooden posts and thatched roofs, with no floor except for the sand of the beach, and enough room for three bags and three beds. The trip was fantastic, except that Craig got some kind of mouth infection swimming through raw sewage on the second-last day. Our next stop was

Cartagena, Colombia, where we met up with a girl Craig had travelled with in Mexico. It was then that Isabella emailed to say she was excited to hear from me, but that Way of the Spirit was fully booked until October. I wrote back saying I'd sleep on the floor in the Maloka if I had to. Craig, his lady-friend and I quickly relocated from Cartagena further north up the coast of Colombia, but with Craig looking like an AIDS patient, the romance between those two failed to rebloom, and Craig and I decided to make an early departure for Medellin. Hence the taxi cab, cloudy skies, drop in temperature and thoughts of Vincent Chase in a fat suit crying, 'Goal!'

'I might need to break out my jeans tonight, mate,' I say, looking out the window of our taxi. 'My *Medi*-jeans...'

*

In our hostel dining room, I take a long chug from a beer. Craig sips a glass of water. He flinches as the liquid hits his cracked lips. Poor guy. After downing the rest of my beer, I wander over to the drinks fridge, grab another, then pop past the front desk to charge it to my tab. The girl in front of me at the desk is buying a bottle of water.

'Oh-kay, so one water,' says the gorgeous Latina girl at reception. 'I jus' need to charge to you name? Is Julia right?'

'Actually, it's Moon River,' says the girl ahead of me, who happens to be wearing yoga pants. 'I was recently given that name by my spiritual teacher.'

'Oh, oh-kay,' says the gorgeous Latina girl. 'But I am sorry, we has to put Julia, because of the system.'

'The *system*,' I say, nodding and pretend-frowning. Moon River leaves with her water. I flash my beer. 'Just this one thanks.'

'It's Nicholas, right?'

She knows my name.

'Actually, you have to call me Nighthawk.'

*

The next day Craig takes a taxi to a doctor's office, and I take a trip to the local mall. The shopping centre is like any other in the world with all the flashing signs and lights, white floors, clothes shops, food courts, sports shops, people dressed nicely in polo shirts and floral dresses, fat people, security guards, young people dressed by an algorithm and couples walking hand-in-hand. I stumble across Panamericana, a bookstore the size of an Officeworks, and begin to wander the aisles until I get a distinct signal from my bowels. My slow search for books becomes a more pressing search for the toilets. The shopping centre becomes a labyrinth. I fret through the couples walking hand in hand and the fat people and the groups of robot kids. Everywhere is black hair, moustaches, perfume and aftershave. Up the escalator. Spinning around in the maze. Back down the escalator. I spot a sign. I'm headed in the right direction. I find the toilets. Into the cubicle. There's no toilet paper. *What the fuck?* I burst out and search the bathroom. No toilet paper anywhere. *How do these mutherfuckers shit?* Out of the bathroom. I need a supermarket. I ask a security guard. He has a moustache. A nice one too. Well groomed. He points. I follow. Supermarket. Walking the aisles. Guessing. Fresh produce. Washing powder. Paper towels. Alcohol. Kitchen supplies. Individual packets of facial tissues! To the counter. Hurry up and take my money. Keep the fucking change. To the bathroom. Empty cubicle, thank fuck. Take my shit. Wipe my arse. Wash my hands. Back past the security guard with the excellent moustache. Back to Panamericana.

And now I can relax and take my time to walk the aisles of books. The English section is vast and well-manicured. I wander for almost an hour and eventually purchase *The Catcher in the Rye* and *The Unbearable Lightness of Being*.

Outside the shopping centre, chuffed at my recent purchases, I'm mobbed by a group of enthusiastic and bright-eyed teenagers. They start speaking in Spanish, so I have to hold up my hands and say, '*no hablas Español*,' which sends them into a frenzy. A middle-aged woman explains to me they're offering hugs for a donation. I'm not sure what they're raising money for but I'm getting very much swept up in the excitement of the hugs. I reach into my wallet and pull out a charitable chunk of Colombian pesos, to cheers from the young people. I'm showered in hugs and admittedly, it all makes me feel rather wonderful.

*

Later in the evening I join a few people from the hostel at a bar while Craig stays behind to get some rest. I wake up naked on my top bunk, stinking of vodka and fried chicken and feeling like a vacuum cleaner's sucked all the moisture out of my face. Once I've had a chance to recover, Craig and I head off on an adventure to find the cable car that sails up the hill over the favelas.

'How're you feeling, mate?' asks Craig as we sway about in the train on the way to the cable car station.

'Like I copped a hatchet to the head.'

'Yeah, you don't look that great.'

'Gee thanks. Did you manage to swing past a mirror this morning? Because you know you look like the guy from *Into the Wild*, after he eats the poisonous berries.'

Craig can't help but laugh at that one. 'Not great news from the doctor yesterday,' he says. 'Prescribed a week of antibiotics and rest.'

I nod and frown. 'Sucks.'

'I'm gonna take it easy for a while and focus on getting healthy.'

'Fair enough. I probably need to slow down on the booze myself. Need to prepare for the jungle. I got an email from Isabella this morning saying they've had a cancellation at Way of the Spirit, so there's a place for me.'

My initial reaction to the email was excitement but having let the news sink in for a while, all those old questions of anxiety and purpose and meditation and diet have bubbled back up to the surface. I can already feel the impact of the big city on my nervous system, after the calming effect of the San Blas Islands. It was something about sun and space and open water that was very healing for me.

'How do you feel about going back to the centre?' asks Craig.

'I'm a bit nervous, but it feels right. It kinda feels like it was inevitable that I'd go back there, like I had unfinished business. Once I got over the whole money thing, it was a pretty easy decision.'

'Is it expensive?'

'Yeah. It'll mean I'll have no savings when I get back home.'

'But who knows when you'll go on another trip like this, right?'

'Exactly. I'm excited to meet up with all my friends from the centre again and hang out. To be honest, I am apprehensive about drinking ayahuasca again.'

'Did you ever get nervous last time you stayed there?'

'Big time. Every ceremony I was shitting myself at least a little bit.'

'I guess that's a healthy approach.'

We watch the colours of the neighbourhoods melt into each other as we fly by. When the train stops, we follow the crowd out of the station and navigate our way to the cable car that links two parts of the city over a large slice of favela. Down below, houses with red brick walls and flat tin roofs are stacked haphazardly on top of each other. Power lines run through the narrow streets, above teenagers playing soccer, their goals set in the middle of the road. Some of the red-brick buildings have flat concrete roofs, and people sit on deck chairs next to chimneys, piles of bricks, stray dogs and clothes-lines. At the top of the hill, we stroll around for a while before finding a shady patch of grass to relax upon.

'I kissed the most gorgeous milf at a nightclub last night,' I say, hands behind my head, gazing up into the sky. 'Her name was Maya. She didn't speak a word of English.'

'How do you know she was a milf then?'

'I convinced this random gay dude to translate a conversation between us.'

'Why did he have to be a gay dude?'

'I didn't have to convince a *gay* dude, necessarily, I just had to convince *some*one to translate and this dude happened to be gay. But anyway, through my gay translator, I said to this girl: "You are the most beautiful girl I have seen in Medellin." And I meant it. I think the language barrier helped. In Australia, if I were to say, *You are the most beautiful girl in Perth*, she'd probably go: *Yeah right mate, whatever, how 'bout you go fuck yourself ya sleaze-bag.'*

We laugh.

'And then she'd glass ya,' says Craig.

*

On my last day in Medellin, Craig and I go out to a café in a part of town where beautiful, well-dressed people frequent. As we wait for our coffees, I think about the day I missed my flight in San José. Some people say, 'Things happen for a reason.' I don't. To say that things happen for a reason implies that our lives are predetermined, that there is some intelligence that's figured everything out already and we are merely carrying out *its* plan. I don't believe that. But I do believe we have the power to draw our own meaning and significance from events. I fucked up in San José, but once I got over it, I had a great time at the hostel and appreciated the bus ride the next day. I missed the boat trip in Tamarindo, but if I'd arrived on time, I would've been faced with the dilemma of whether to drop acid with the boys. Did I miss the plane 'for a reason'? Who the hell could say such a thing?

A beautiful and voluptuous woman brings our coffee and fills our glasses with water. Both Craig and I smile at her until she leaves our table.

'How's the whole abstinence thing going?' asks Craig.

I shake my head. 'It's no picnic. I was reflecting the other day about how I used to organise my whole week around sex. I'd have dates and hook-ups all mapped out in my calendar.'

'Sounds great.'

'Yeah, it was, but also, it was taking the priority of my life, and I'm not sure if that's the best way I can spend my time?

217

Well, maybe *sex* is the best way I can spend my time. But not *organising* it.'

'Still less work than a relationship.'

'You're the one writing the book.'

'On break-ups, mate. Not relationships.'

I laugh. 'Do you know the comedian Bill Hicks?'

'Not really. Go on anyway.'

'There's a bit that he does that goes something like this: "It's hard to have a relationship in this business. You're always travelling and keeping weird hours. It's gonna take a very special woman… Or, a bunch of average ones."'

Craig chuckles. To laugh would mean cracking open his lips.

'I'm noticing that it feels different being abstinent compared to just not getting laid. I haven't had sex in almost two months, and that's a long time for me, especially in recent history. But I'm not frustrated. Don't get me wrong, I'd love to have sex, but it's not the same feeling of frustration when you're trying to get laid and can't. I'm realising how much I defined myself in the past through my ability to get laid. My sense of masculinity was dependent on it. My self-esteem, mood, everything was dependent on it. When I was getting laid, I felt like a superstar. When I wasn't, I went fucken crazy! I want to change that. I want to feel complete and confident in myself, so I don't need a woman to make me feel like a man.'

Craig nods and makes that frowny-face that means you agree with what the person is saying.

'One of the ideas I got out of the ayahuasca centre,' I say, 'was to learn how to be complete and whole in myself. When you're complete in yourself, then you can attract someone who is also complete in *them*selves. If you are incomplete, then all you attract is other damaged, incomplete people, looking for someone else to fill the hole inside them. Until we are complete, we're destined to be disappointed because no-one can fill the hole inside us except ourselves.'

'That's a pretty grim thought.'

'Makes sense though. We've just been sold this fairy-tale of meeting 'the one' person who will complete us and make it all better.'

I pay for the coffees, and Craig wraps me up in a hug.

'Best of luck in the jungle,' says Craig. 'I'm really glad you decided to come up to Costa Rica.'

'Me too, mate. Best of luck in Colombia.'

'Get in touch if you're ever in Sydney.'

'You'll be the first to know.'

Part Four
The Return
September 2016

Chapter Twenty
...once more down the rabbit hole.

Twilight descends around the Maloka. It seems a lifetime since I was here. Tony pours the brew and hands the cup to me. I lift it to my mouth, close my eyes, whisper a prayer to Pachamama and drink my medicine.

... once more down the rabbit hole.

Tony has me staying at Pentagram. It's a one-bed wooden cabin nestled into the jungle. There's a stream running past at the rear and a tight balcony leading to the bathroom. Earlier this afternoon, when I was lying on my bed and staring up at the ceiling, I spotted a pair of white-bellied rats crawling around in the roof. I figured the rats would eat the things I *really* don't want in my house. Except for the snakes. Snake beats rat. Thoughts of Jasper came to me like apparitions this afternoon. He was staying at Pentagram when I was at the centre last time. I liked Jasper at first, but he did tend to tell the same stories over and over again. 'Never use toilet cubicle number one!' he'd say. 'If anything ever happens during a ceremony, it always happens in cubicle number one!' The last time I saw him was in Pentagram. He seemed frustrated. He mentioned he was going to ask Tony if he could work at Way of the Spirit. I guess it didn't work out for him.

Tony asks if anyone would like another cup, and I'm up there without a second thought. It's just me and one other drinking tonight, a new girl who I haven't had a chance to introduce myself to yet. It looked like she was doing yoga postures in the dark before the ceremony.

I stayed two nights in Iquitos before coming here. I needed some time to readjust to isolation and contemplation, and to catch up on my journaling. The 'holiday' with Craig and Glassy was just what I needed, a break from my head and a reminder that travelling is supposed to be fun, that *life* is supposed to be fun. I fucked up the drugs and alcohol part of the post-diet rules, but I stayed abstinent, and feel like I'm really over the hump with all that, so to speak…

Each morning in Iquitos, that same old guy was sitting out the front of Dawn on the Amazon, wearing his cargo shorts, short sleeve button-up shirt and skipper's cap. I'd give him a little nod like I was a local. I couldn't grow old out here. This jungle is beautiful, but the city is too grimy for my blood.

I get up to take a piss. My limbs feel heavy, and the world is tilting on a weird axis. The new girl is deep in the medicine, no doubt about it – it sounds like she's having an orgasm.

Ellie came to see me this afternoon. I gave her the chocolate I bought from the Belen Markets, and she kissed me on the cheek. I considered telling her about all the 'dreams' but thought better of it. I asked if she was going to be in ceremony tonight, but she said she and Isabella were reading each other's Tarot instead.

There's commotion over by the new girl. Her orgasms turned to tears then to moans and for the last few minutes she's been wailing. Tony's doing some kind of shamanic work on her. The medicine's coming on strong for me as well now. Pounding, metronomic synthesiser sounds rattle against my eardrums, drowning out faint whisperings of the *Language*. Now wild fractal visionscapes open up around me but then *Crack!* as if by an outlaw's lasso, I'm wrenched back into the room by a shooting pain in my belly. I want to dive deeper into this psychedelic experience, but my stomach is swelling and gurgling, and I have to get to the bathroom soon or the medicine will take over and I'll shit myself. I stumble around in the dark until I reach the toilet. With my pants around my ankles and torch in my mouth, I scan the cubicle for spiders, but before I've searched two corners the shit begins to flood out of me. I drop my torch to the floor and induce vomit. Liquid muck and shit and vomit and piss flows out of me, gushing into buckets at either end of my body. Now, the walls of the cubicle start to vibrate, and the Fear comes in fast…

…You'll be in this toilet forever.

Wait. What number am I in?

You're in number one, dumb-dumb. You. Are. Fucked.

That's bullshit. Jasper was full of shit.

Who's Jasper?

Stop it.

Seriously. Who's Jasper? You're *the one staying in Pentagram… What if* you *are Jasper? What if you never actually left the centre? Think about it, man. You know it's true.*

This is stupid. Seriously. Fuck off.

*

225

Paulo sings his final song to close the ceremony, and Tony brings around a bag of mandarins. I lean against the wall and take a sip of water.

'How was your night, Nick?' he asks.

'A whole lot of purging,' I say, 'but I think I'm out of it now, although, now… that… I'm… saying… it… the… medicine… is… starting… to… kick… in…again.'

I leave my mandarin on the floor and slide back down onto my mat and rest my head on the pillow while the voices carry on away in the distance.

*

Sam enters the Maloka with Gaia. I didn't think he'd still be here at the Centre. He moves over to talk with Tony and Paulo. A wolf spider scuttles along the wooden floorboards. It turns to face me; the candlelight behind it casting a grotesque shadow. I shoo the creature away with my mind.

Sam checks on the new girl then drifts over to sit beside me, eager to discuss my travels through Central America. I get through half a sentence before my words turn to jelly.

'I'm sorry, man,' he says. 'Are you still in the medicine?'

'Yeah, I guess, I'm – mumble mumble, blah blah blurb…'

'We can catch up properly tomorrow, dude.'

'Mumph,' I say, and collapse back onto my mat.

Dark clouds. Storms. Murky writhing seaweed. And then black and white images of childhood. I'm alone playing with my toys in the living room. I'm on the front yard of my grandparent's house, and my friend is sitting away from me crying. I'm alone on the front yard swatting flies with a stick and talking to myself. My parents are fighting in the laundry. My sister and I are sharing a room at my grandparent's house, and I'm on the top bunk. I've been crying, but quietly, so my sister doesn't hear me. My father arrives home from work late and when he comes into our room, I pretend I'm asleep. He kisses me on the forehead and all I want is for him to pick me up and take me away, but I pretend I can't hear him. I want to talk to him so badly, but I can't open my mouth. I'm trying to be strong for him. I don't want to bother him. I don't want to be trouble for my parents. I'm an adult on the mat in the ceremony and I'm a child in bed and my father is in the room and I want to tell him I'm unhappy and I miss him and I want him to play with me, but my mouth won't open. I hold on. I hold on. He says goodnight. And now he's gone. I turn to face the wall and I'm so sad I want to throw up. I choke back my tears and I die inside.

*

Through tiny slits in my eyelids, I make out my ash bowl next to my mat. My hands respond to my brain signals, and they move up to my face – which feels strangely novel and foreign – to wipe the tears from my eyes. I drag myself up to lean against the wall and reach for a mapacho. My fingers ferry the stick of tobacco to my mouth, and I light and inhale the smoke. I take a sip of water from my bottle then look over to see Sam still sitting with Christal. Tony and Paulo are gone.

Sam waves. 'How you doin' buddy?'

I smile and wave back. 'I'm alive.'

'I'm Christal,' says the new girl when I eventually summon the strength to sit with them. 'I was just saying to Sam that I heard him and some of the other guys staying here talking about this 'breakthrough' experience, and I didn't really know what they were talking about. But then tonight, that was *it*! It wasn't what I expected. But now I know. You know?'

Sam starts laughing.

'You know what I'm talking about, Nicholas?'

'Yes, I know.' I'm speaking slowly, but the right words are coming out, which is a good sign. 'I've sat in over ten ceremonies now, I think. I'd say only two or three of them have been 'breakthrough' experiences. I've learned something from every ceremony, but it's just, those big ones are so much more... dramatic.' I try my best to recount the story of my second ceremony at Way of the Spirit, with all the anxiety and primitive monkeys and cascading neon fractals and magic carpets and *transcendence*... 'And then this guy *saved* me,' I say, pointing to Sam.

'Oh man, I was so fucking *deep* in the medicine that night. Nick, I think you and I were riding the same wave, but I'd just hopped off about an hour before you.'

'Dunno if I was riding it, mate. More like holding on for dear life.'

A shadow stirs on the floor of the Maloka. Christal shrieks and Gaia barks. I jump to my feet. Two wolf spiders are on the loose. We follow them with torchlight. I toss Sam an empty bucket and one wolf is trapped. The other escapes towards a wall. A job for the cleaners tomorrow.

'Oh guys,' says Sam, as we take the path back to our houses, 'I just remembered something from the last ceremony. So, it's the end of the night and all I want is to go to bed. I'm not out of the medicine but decide to walk back to my room anyway.'

'Are you sure you should be telling this story right now?' says Christal.

Sam smiles. 'I get about halfway along the wooden path and I stop and think to myself: "Sweet Jesus, Sam, how long have you been walking along this path?" I keep walking and walking and walking forever. No matter how long I walk, I never get to the end of the path. It's like I'm stuck in a time-loop. You probably know where this is going... I stop to sit down on one of the benches and fall asleep. And I wake up the next morning in the Maloka.'

*

Upstairs at the Big House, Sam and I lounge across beanbags and smoke mapachos while we catch up properly on events from the last month. Despite the difficulty of last night's ceremony, I'm feeling chipper this morning. Ellie paid me a visit earlier on while I was still at Pentagram. Actually, she tried to secretly drop off a note while I was in the shower, but Gaia barked and blew her cover. Ellie's face was bright, and her hair was fluffy and wild, and there was a kind of vibrant glow around her.

At breakfast, I introduced myself to Margaret, a middle-aged Israeli woman with long black hair, and I saw Christal for the first time in the light of day. She has blonde hair and a kind face, though her skin is covered in a red rash that she's clearly self-conscious about. She thanked me for hanging out with her last night and showed me some pictures of her kids on her phone. Tony popped in to tell me he's been brewing up a plant especially for me called chiric sanango.

'How's it been with the medicine?' I ask Sam, after swatting a mosquito, lighting a fresh mapacho and sinking a little deeper into my beanbag.

'Powerful,' he says. 'I went super hard while you were away, going to as many ceremonies as I could. But I'm starting to cool off now. No need to rush.'

I strip off my shirt and lay it down on the beanbag to stop my skin from sticking to the material.

'What's your intention now that you're back, Nick?'

'I don't know if I have a clear intention this time around. I came to Way of the Spirit in the first place looking for personal growth and self-awareness and self-control, that type of thing. I wanted to somehow figure out the cause of my anxiety and depression.'

Sam nods with recognition.

'I used to go into ceremonies with an intention,' I say. 'I remember before my second ceremony I went in like: "Show me this is real."'

'How'd that go?'

'*Too* real.'

We both laugh.

'I've thought about going in with a question,' I say. 'But then I remember this Terence McKenna lecture where he says something like, "I was going through a period of personal difficulty, so I prepared a question to ask the mushroom. During the trip I asked, 'Am I doing the right thing?' To which the mushroom replied, 'What kind of a chickenshit question is that to ask an extraterrestrial entelechy?'" So, I'm just gonna go in there open-minded and hope for the best.'

Chapter Twenty-One
Chiric Sanango

Tony, sitting on the wooden floorboards with his feet planted and his knees pointing up to the white-bellied rats in the ceiling of Pentagram, holds out a bowl with my first dose of chiric sanango. He watches as I pour it down the hatch.

'Was there tobacco in that?'

'Yes,' he says, smiling. 'A few other plants as well.'

I think Tony puts tobacco in everything.

Reminded by pangs of tobacco-nausea, I ask Tony for his guidance with regards to inducing vomit at the later stages of an ayahuasca journey. 'Like, if I'm feeling that I need to purge,' I say, 'but it's just not coming up.'

'I wouldn't induce,' he says, shaking his head. 'Sit with the discomfort. Don't try to escape from it. Feel into it. Practice listening to your body because it's trying to tell you something.'

I thought he might say something like that.

'Now,' says Tony, 'Chiric sanango is a relaxing plant medicine, but it can make you a bit, how can I say... *wobbly*. So, watch your balance.'

He smiles, and then he's gone.

Pentagram is colder than Casa del Graham, so in the afternoon, I take a stroll down my front path and sit in the sun to smoke a mapacho and watch the ants. In the treetops there's a band of little red monkeys patrolling. I haven't seen these guys since Casa del Graham. My head spins.

In the early evening, I retreat to my bed. My sheets stink of jungle plants and testosterone. The young women bring vegetable juice and porridge. 'Hola,' I mumble. The girls leave the jug and bowl on my writing table.

I contemplate the effort required to move. Waves of nausea and weakness. Pins and needles all over my skin. Not worth it.

Pentagram, being closely surrounded by trees, quickly becomes dark as the sun sets. I light candles and place them around my room. I take a candle out to the bathroom for my shower. When I return to bed, my body is shaking. Not cold, not hot, not anxious. I just feel very strange...

*

When I wake up, my mind is tired, and the muscles around my temples are tender. My night was thick with dreams. They were so vivid, so real. I clamber for my journal, but alas, the dreams vanish like spectres into shadow.

Pentagram stands between Tony's house and the path to the Maloka so I can hear people as they pass by. I can see them too, when they're in the right spot.

That's Sam and Ellie on their way to breakfast.

Tony will be on his way to my place soon.

A gecko chases a moth around the outside of my flywire walls.

'Nick?' comes a call, and then Tony appears at my door.

I ask how last night's ayahuasca ceremony went. Tony shakes his head, then slings himself into my hammock, like an old friend sinking into the couch with a beer.

'There was a young couple, new to the centre,' he says. 'They had a lovers' quarrel and turned the night into a circus. We had to kick them out of the Maloka in the end. This place is not for beginners. I can do without that kind of drama.' Tony lights his mapacho then leans into the hammock and looks up at the ceiling. 'I love these old houses with the thatched roofs.'

Down on the floor with my smouldering mapacho I nod, unconvinced.

'The problem is,' he says, 'they're just perfect for all kinds of animals and insects. That's why we're not doing thatched roofs for any of the new buildings.'

'I spotted some rats in the roof.'

'The locals eat the rats, you know. They're not bad. Much healthier than city rats. Out here they've got a good diet. There's all sorts of things in these roofs. Snakes, spiders, all kinds of bugs.'

Awesome…

Tony pours my medicine, watches me drink, and then he leaves.

I pass the time by writing in my journal and reading *The Unbearable Lightness of Being*. I like writing in exercise books. There's something special about crafting the words with my hand. Watching the ink take form on the page. My handwriting has distinct style and character, unlike the homogenised fonts of a word processor. My sweat seeps into the pages of my journals. It's a magical, alchemical transmission of thought into matter. I like reading physical books too. I feel about books, the same way that Tereza from *Unbearable Lightness* does – walking down the street with one tucked under my arm. I love the feel of a book after I've read it and left my mark on it. I like when the book has my dog-eared pages and my hand-written notes down the margins and my creases and bends. My books travel with me; they see the different rooms that I stay in, they see the beaches and the mountains and the forests. We form a physical and philosophical collaboration.

Sam's question the other day about my intentions here has me thinking. It hasn't really been like I thought it would be. I don't know what exactly I was expecting ayahuasca to be like. Not like this. It doesn't matter. I know that I have to be here, now, and that something important is going to happen.

I remember being at a party back in Perth, talking with a girl who went to school with Will, the former manager at Way of the Spirit, who I never actually met. When I told this girl I was going to the jungle to drink ayahuasca, she said, 'Be careful, Nick! You don't want to turn out like Will. He went crazy. He wants to live in the jungle now.' People back home don't understand the calling. 'Be careful!' they say. *You fucking be careful!* That's what I wanted to say to them. *Don't worry about me. You be careful you don't live your whole goddamn life in the matrix…*

People back home don't get it. They said I was 'lucky' to be travelling. What's luck got to do with it? Sure, I won the fucken genetic and geographic lottery when I came into this world in King Edward Memorial Hospital in Perth rather than the floor of a shanty-house in the slums of Mumbai. So, I'm lucky in that sense. But I didn't win this trip in a fucken magazine competition. I'm travelling because of a series of decisions. I *decided* to work my arse off and save all my money instead of spending it on whatever-the-fuck people waste their money on. I decided to rent a cheap room at my mate's place rather than getting my own place or God forbid, laying a deposit down on a house. And then I *decided* to give up the security of my full-time job so I could create the time to travel. I *decided* to sell my car and any other possessions worth anything, so I'd have enough money. I *decided* to compromise my relationships for freedom. In this life, you make your own goddamn luck.

I sit in the afternoon sunshine smoking a mapacho while the bronze-skinned ladies clean my room. I spot a grey lizard crawling up a thin tree between the path and my little wooden house. The lizard starts nodding its head back and forth. Then a bright orange disc fans out from under its neck. The sun is pleasant on my skin but feels stronger than usual. My lips are tingling, but that could be from the nicotine in my mapacho. I feel light-headed and woozy, like maybe I could purge. Strong vibrations are running up and down my body.

*

Yesterday was hot and uncomfortable, but it rained last night, so there's a coolness and calmness to the forest this morning. Tony tells me he spoke with the spirit of his dead grandmother while he was drinking chiric ten years ago. 'I've communicated with many different spirits on this land,' he says.

I've spent most of the time communicating with my pillow.

'There's a jungle spirit that wanders through here sometimes,' he says, pointing out past my balcony. 'The spirit hates deforestation. He hates the killing of animals without eating them. He's also a trickster.'

'Sounds like Pan.'

'That's right.' Tony nods and smiles. 'The spirits out here will help you if they like you, Nick. But if they don't like you, then they'll fuck with you.'

I look out into the trees around my house. *Do you like me, spirits?*

'Once, here in Iquitos,' he says. 'Something from the trees took a child away into the jungle for three days. When she returned, she told her family she'd been taken by gnomes.'

I drink my third cup.

'How are you feeling?' asks Tony.

'I'm feeling really weak, actually. And my whole body is tingling.'

'That's normal. The Chiric is building up in your system. Feel into what comes up. Now, I'm going into town for a couple of days, so Charlie will deliver the rest of your diet.'

Tony leaves and I sling out on my hammock. It'll be good to check in with Charlie again. I'm itching to reconnect with Ellie and Isabella as well. But for now, I'm on my own. On my own with the rats and the spiders.

I flick through my journal. There's a rough scratching I made from a dream last night: *Syd Drumstick. The sexy one.* That's all I wrote. I remember my friend Stan yelling this at me in the dream. 'Remember Syd Drumstick!' He was talking about Syd Barrett, the original front man for Pink Floyd. It's one of those personal jokes that only *you* find funny, and don't really know why. I guess it's important because Syd Barrett lost his mind from taking too much acid. I do wonder sometimes if maybe *I'm* losing my mind. I don't know what the fuck drumsticks have to do with anything.

I shift to lie flat on my bed, with the mozzie net flung open. When I was staying at Casa del Graham, I'd keep my bed fully contained within the mozzie net all day. At Pentagram, I can no longer be bothered. Mozzies only come out at night anyway. I don't know why it's even called a mosquito net. It should be a called a 'wolf spider and snake' net.

God, I'm so fucking hungry. What would I eat if I could have anything? Chicken noodle soup, ceviche and rice paper rolls. Yes. That's what I'd eat. I'd boil the chicken in a broth and shred the meat for the soup and for the rice paper rolls. I'd add a dash of coconut milk to the ceviche to offset the acidity of the lime juice. I'd use a little freshly squeezed orange juice in the ceviche as well. And sliced mango. Sliced shallots. Diced salmon fillets or king fish. In the soup would go the shredded chicken, rice noodles, shitake mushrooms, thinly sliced shallots, lemongrass, ginger, garlic and chilli. For the rice paper rolls, I'd layer chicken, lettuce, rice noodles, bean sprouts, coriander and mint. Any leftover lettuce and vegetables can go in a salad with soy sauce, chilli, garlic, ginger and lime juice. Any leftover mango can go with vanilla ice-cream for dessert.

Lunch arrives at half past twelve.

One jug of carrot juice.

Fuck me.

*

At around two-thirty in the afternoon, Charlie the coca shaman greets me with a broad smile and my fourth dose of chiric.

'How's it going, Nick?' he says.

'G'day Charlie, great to see you. I'd give you a hug, but, you know.'

He smiles and shakes the bottle of jungle brew in his hand then takes a seat in front of me on the floor. Charlie says his own set of prayers and incantations, similar though different to Tony's, while he chews coca and wafts tobacco smoke around himself and over the freshly poured bowl of chiric.

He hands me the bowl and I drink.

'Hey Charlie,' I say, when I've had some water and shaken off the initial nausea of the medicine. 'If you've got time this morning, I'd love to hear a little about your shamanic training.'

'Sure.' He settles into the floor and lights a mapacho like Gandalf lighting a fresh bowl of pipe-weed, and I settle in for a story like I'm Frodo Baggins. 'I started my training in the UK with some local shamans. Part of my training was theoretical, like learning the medicine wheel, and the various animal spirits and the archetypes. And part of the training was practical. We used non-medicine techniques, things like sensory deprivation, vision quests, hunger fasts. We'd stay out in the forest alone for seven days without food. Or, we'd stay in a dark room for days at a time, with someone slipping a plate of food through a little gap under a door.'

'Why would you *do* that?'

'It's about changing up the regular patterns of the body and the mind. We wanted to break apart the layers of conditioning. What are the cultural imprints? What's from the family bloodlines. What's mine on a *soul* level? And then the question is: What can I let go of? We get *stuck* in our normal everyday routines, Nick. These techniques work to break us out of those patterns to bring us face-to-face with all the shit that our mind does such a great job of hiding.'

'What was the most challenging technique you tried?'

Charlie contemplates the question for a moment then says, 'After training for a number of years, I decided to take on this one particular level of sensory deprivation. I didn't do this straight away, mind you. I worked my way up to it. What I did was lie down in a coffin and have it nailed shut from the outside.' *Ugh...* 'And then I was buried two metres underground, with just a long, thin metal straw running up from the coffin out through the earth to give me oxygen. I stayed like that for twenty-four hours.'

*

I wake up drenched in sweat. In my dream, I was trapped in an asylum surrounded by people who were familiar but unrecognisable.

I take a sip of water and thank the stars for my freedom.

I have a strange, irresistible, niggling suspicion that my life is merely another layer of a dream, and that one day, I'm going to wake up from it. It's a fascinating and terrifying notion.

'I've been shitting a lot,' I say to Charlie when he arrives at Pentagram with the fifth dose of chiric. 'Like five a day.'

'That's good,' he says. 'The medicine is moving straight through you, without getting blocked.'

How wonderful for me. 'It tastes stronger today,' I say, wincing as I take down the bowl of brown liquid.

'It *is* stronger,' he replies, nodding and chewing his coca, mapacho hanging out the side of his mouth. 'The brew continues to ferment each day and becomes more intensified.'

'So, it's like eating a curry the next day?'

'Yeah, that's right,' he says. He's British so he knows exactly what the fuck I'm talking about. Charlie leaves, chewing coca, smiling to himself and nodding away as if he's aware of some universal truth that has yet to be revealed to me.

I sit on the toilet for the second time this morning.

Nausea and shitting. This is my life now.

*

Charlie delivered the sixth cup yesterday afternoon, and I tossed and turned in bed for the next ten hours with electric, vibrating skin. This morning, he gave me my seventh and final cup, and wished me good luck in tonight's ceremony. Now I'm sitting on my rocking chair watching a gecko stalk a moth. I blink, and they both vanish. Ellie left me a note this morning asking if I'd like to do a Tarot reading when I've finished my diet. I miss her. Outside my house, a rooster fucks an outcast black hen. The tingling sensation on my skin has become very uncomfortable, overwhelming even. This medicine is like acupuncture all over my body, all the time. I want to move. I feel cooped up in here. *Hah! Cooped.* But I have no energy. I feel sick all the time. Like I could spew. All the time. So many shits. I'm sick of this fucking vegetable juice. I drink water and rock on my chair. I grab my bucket and hold it on my lap. I burp and spit thick saliva. Another drink of water. More burping and spitting. Another drink of water. I wait and I wait, and I sit with the discomfort. I drink water. And eventually, out it comes. Gushing tobacco-bile and burning acidic mandarin. Then relief. Done. No more chiric.

*

After my second cup of ayahuasca, and after the waves of nausea have passed, the medicine starts to grind me down deep into the floor. My body is heavy, and I sink, as though into dark quicksand. I don't struggle. I allow myself to be squished into the earth. The medicine then takes hold of my heart and pulls me up out of the mud. The medicine tries to lift me up into a beautiful golden orb of light, but I can't go with it. Instead, my body begins to segment itself. Parts of me rise towards the light, and parts of me, my stomach and intestines, sink down into the mud, and I am slowly, painlessly, ripped apart.

I retire to the bathroom to purge an enormous volume of liquid shit.

Chapter Twenty-Two
Tarot & Kambo

It took a few days to recover but now the chiric has oozed out of my system, and there's a spring in my step as I enjoy the freedom of a stroll away from Pentagram along the winding paths of Way of the Spirit towards Ellie's house. She's still staying in Fleur, just down the path from my old place, Casa del Graham. For the past two days now, I've visited Ellie in her room to smoke mapachos and talk.

The first day we spoke about religion.

My father was baptised Greek Orthodox, though he only went to church for weddings and funerals. My mother was a recovering Irish Catholic. My parents loosely held their respective faiths – perhaps out of social obligation, but mostly out of fear, I suspect, and felt it necessary that I should learn these tribal superstitions as well. When I was ten years old, my parents pulled me out of the state school where I was floundering and enrolled me into a Catholic boys' school where we had to go to church once a week. I hated it. The priest was so smug and self-righteous. And all the images of the tortured

Christ made me sick. Even the smell was nauseating. My parents were going through a divorce at the time, and there was something about going to the church that brought all that pain to the surface. I could hide my tears by hanging my head down between my knees and pretending I was so bored I was falling asleep. If the other boys knew I was crying, I'd be dead. Despite my resistance, I remember being curious leading up to my first Mass. The priest had been building it up so much I wondered what it would feel like. Most of the other boys had already taken Mass years before. They seemed to just be going through the motions. I remember taking the cracker from the priest and placing it on my tongue. I took a sip from the golden chalice. Sour wine. The body and the blood of Christ. Nothing happened... Just as I thought. A load of bullshit.

The second day, Ellie and I spoke about relationships.

This discussion was far more challenging for me. It took almost two hours for me to work up the courage, but eventually, I told her about my infidelity and how I broke the best thing going for me in my life. I was still in love with Jessica the whole time, and yet. And yet. And yet...

I held onto the lie until it began to eat away at my stomach like a cancer, and I knew that I could bear the guilt no longer.

I told Ellie about the moment when I watched Jessica's heart break before my eyes.

'So that's me,' I said to Ellie. 'A piece of shit.'

Ellie took a tedious draw from her mapacho before blowing it purposely in my face. 'Look,' she said to me, half-smiling, half-lecturing, 'it was a shitty thing for you to do. A really shitty thing to do. A total dick move. But you're not a piece of shit. You're a person. People make mistakes. The real question is, have you learned from your mistake?'

I nodded and made a frowny face.

'Have you learned?' she said abruptly, 'I'm asking you, now. Have you learned? Have you cheated again?'

'No. Never. I'll never make that mistake again,' I said.

'Well, okay then. You've learned your lesson. Time to forgive yourself.'

I pass through a tunnel of overhanging branches and dodge a precession of ants underfoot. Ellie's place is shaded and secluded. I kick my thongs off on her front porch and knock on her window. Today, Ellie and I are going to do a Tarot reading.

'Come in, Nicky,' she says.

Inside it smells of freshly burned sage and Palo Santo wood. Bottles of moisturiser and essential oils cover the ledges. Coloured blankets and mats lie on the floors. Clear plastic boxes sit against the walls overflowing with clothes. Books lie in piles on the floor. And, sitting cross-legged on her bed in a flowing green dress, with her curly black hair fanning out like a crazed scientist, is Ellie. We hug on the bed, and I hand her some mapacho and chocolate that I brought in exchange for the reading.

'Have you ever done Tarot?' she asks.

'I haven't. My mum and sister get into it. Not me though.'

'What's your star sign?'

'I'm on the cusp between Aries and Taurus, which kind of predisposes me to question the validity of the whole thing.'

'You're *such* an Aries.'

I roll my eyes. 'Ellie, I can't accept that the position of the stars at my birth determines my personality. And I guess I should be honest with you now; I struggle to see how someone can predict my future based on what cards are drawn.'

'You don't have to look at it like that, Nicky. What if these cards are just a base from which you can ask questions about your life? The way a psychologist might use a Rorschach Test. Maybe my skill in drawing the cards has nothing to do with my ability to predict your future, but instead, is just about me tuning in to your energy, asking the right questions and helping you to draw your own conclusions.'

Ellie shuffles through her deck and fishes out one card, placing it down in front of me. Decans of Aries. The card is drenched in red and fire and holds beautiful, complex imagery. There are classic ram's horns at the top, and below them a double-headed eagle. In the centre of the card are two intertwining snakes. At the base of the image is one open eye. I look up to Ellie. 'Is this a traditional deck?'

'Kind of. It has all the same cards as a traditional deck, but the images are different. I found this deck online and resonated with the artwork. Now, when you draw a card, I will give my interpretation, but it is useful for you to consider what you are drawn to in the images.'

Ellie lights a piece of Palo Santo then tumbles the smoke over her skin. She wafts the burning wood over her set of Tarot cards and then passes the piece of wood to me. I run the smouldering stick over my body, then lay the wood down in my ash bowl and light up a mapacho. Ellie closes her eyes and starts praying in English and I think Spanish and maybe another language I don't recognise. I take a draw from my mapacho. She holds the set of cards against her breast.

Her eyes flash open. 'Are you ready?'

'Yes.'

Ellie hands me her deck and asks me to shuffle until I feel the cards aligning with my energy. When it is time, I should draw one card and place it face down in front of me to represent my present, then draw another two cards and place them either side to represent my past and my future. I close my eyes and breathe, silently moving the cards around in my hands. Sceptical thoughts try to invade and belittle the process, but I do my best to let them pass by. When I open my eyes, there are three cards arranged in front of me. The backs of the cards are decorated with the same flashing holograms; images of swords and pentacles, cups and wands, and the letters *ABRAHADABRA* repeated in a cascading pyramid. Ellie smiles to me and nods. I turn the central card.

The Fool.

Ellie laughs.

That'd be right.

'I can't believe you drew The Fool.'

'Are you making fun of me?' I ask, smiling.

'No, I'm not. The Fool is perfect for you. He is at the start of a journey. He is a clean slate with infinite potential.'

Depicted on the face of the card is a shirtless jester with a sack tied to a stick. Admittedly, this is rather appropriate. The Fool is approaching the edge of a portal in space-time, and is followed by a wolf, a dragonfly and two snakes.

'But isn't my journey coming to an end? I've only got a few more weeks here.'

'Perhaps your journey is just beginning?'

I fold over the card to the left. Three of Wands. The image is similar to the Decans of Aries. Another set of ram's horns. More red and more fire. Two more intertwining snakes.

'This card indicates that everything is moving steadily for you now, thanks to your strong foundation and careful planning for the future.'

'I suppose I did a lot of planning to come on this trip. But I don't really have any idea what I'm going to do when I go back home.'

'Then maybe this means you need to make some plans so you are grounded for your return. It is difficult to return to the matrix, Nicky. You need to prepare; otherwise, you may come up against obstacles in your way and this may lead to frustration.'

I consider how well I handled obstacles when I left this place the first time around.

'This card is about forming a vision and a plan for your future. A strong base to launch from.'

I nod silently, then uncover the final card, my future.

Ten of Swords.

In the centre of the card, eight swords have penetrated an egg, and to each side of the egg, a snake has been stabbed into a stone with a sword. In the background, a setting sun is blocked by clouds, and the ground is murky and black.

'That doesn't look great,' I say.

'Okay,' starts Ellie. 'This card is, well, it's a little dark.' Her giggles mask discomfort. 'The Ten of Swords is about failure, defeat and death–'

Wonderful.

'–But this can mean the death of something inside you that no longer serves. It can mean new beginnings. This can be painful, Nicky, but it might mean that it is time for change.'

I light a mapacho and survey my spread. 'This is fucking grim.'

'What are you trying to call into your life, Nicky? What is it that you want for your future?'

'I don't know,' I say.

She sits waiting.

You do know.

'I don't know if I told you this before Ellie, but I'm trying to become a writer.'

'You're *trying* to become a writer? Or, you *are* a writer.'

I never really noticed before how agitating Ellie can be.

'Are you ready to call this in, Nicky? Are there aspects of your life that you need to let go of to allow this to happen for you? In order to become the man you want to be?'

'I don't know,' I say, then take a drag from my mapacho. I stay silent for a while, trying to let go of my frustration. 'Have you read *The Alchemist*?' I ask, eventually.

'Yes, I love this book.'

'You know the character of the merchant, who has the dream of one day going to Mecca?' Ellie nods, so I continue. 'The protagonist, the young boy coming of age, says to the merchant he should just pack up his shop and go. But the merchant prefers to live with the *dream* of Mecca. He prefers to keep it as a fantasy. That way he can't be disappointed with the actual experience.'

'I remember this part.'

'I know what the merchant means. I wrote a novel before I came on this trip. But it was a failure. I'm trying to write another one now. But I don't know if I should even bother. If I can't get it published, then what's the point?'

I take a drag from my mapacho and hope that Ellie will change the subject. She just looks to me expectantly.

'The image of myself as a writer is a fantasy I've created. And I guess, I'm afraid that I'll become like the merchant – and just go on writing half-finished stories and doing some other job, holding onto the *dream* of being a writer until I die.'

'How does it make you feel saying that?'

'It makes me feel sick. I'm scared that I'll waste my life. That I'll get to the end having never even tried.' *Don't cry in front of Ellie.*

'So, what's stopping you?'

I think of the phantom agent from Sydney. 'I don't know.' I fidget on the bed. *Why do women always want to talk so much?* 'Well, it's because I don't really know how to become a professional writer. I don't know anyone in the publishing business. I don't know any agents or editors. I can't call myself a writer because I haven't published anything. I don't know if I'm even any good.'

'Don't you see that you are creating all of these barriers for yourself?'

'What do you mean?'

'You don't have to figure out with your *mind* how to solve all of these problems. Your soul has already revealed your path. You just have to believe in your heart that you are a writer, and all the rest will fall into place.'

That all sounds lovely, but surely, I can't just believe. *I have to actually* do *something. Just believing isn't going to get my novel on the desk of a publisher.*

'All you have to do is commit, Nicky. Believe in your heart, and trust that the universe will deliver when you're ready.'

*

I'm sitting bare-chested and cross-legged on a yoga mat with my back leaning against my bed frame. A bucket sits to my right, and there's a big bottle of water to my left. Tony arrives at the door.

'Come in, mate.'

I continue with breathing exercises while Tony prepares. He applies an alcohol swab to my shoulder. Heart rate intensifying. I can't quite remember what the experience was like the first time. Tony pushes a smouldering incense stick into my flesh to burn off the top layers of skin in five little white dots, just below the scars of the last kambo ceremony.

Inhale.

Exhale.

Tony places the frog poison paste on my open wounds. The blood rushes to my arm and then to my neck and then to my face. Sinking, dreadful panic. I feel my heartbeat in my head. My temples are bursting with molten lava.

Fuck me. Why'd I do this again? Fuck! The pain. It's too much. Take it off. Take it off. Take it off. Take it off!

No! Accept the pain, Nick. You can get through this. Just breathe.

My eyes well with tears. My throat is dry and hot. This is a thick, cloudy, disappointing pain. I lean over and lie on the mat.

All things are impermanent, my brother. This too shall pass.

I pull myself up and I grab my bucket. Out comes breakfast. Burning poison and bile and spirulina smoothie. I struggle to my feet, dizzy and burning.

'You alright, Nicholas?' asks Tony.

'Yeah,' I mutter. 'Bathroom.'

Tony opens the back door for me and guides me out to the bathroom. I drop my shorts and plant myself naked onto the toilet. I rest a spare bucket on my lap and spew some more bile. Ten minutes pass. I pull up my pants, wash my hands and lie down on the bathroom floor. I focus on my breath. Soon, I am calm. The situation has been managed.

Tony pokes his head in through the bathroom door. 'How you doin' in there?'

'I'm alright.'

'Can I come in to wipe off the kambo?'

'Yes, you can.'

*

The following day, feeling both courageous and humbled, I stroll to the Big House for breakfast. After a smoothie I make my way upstairs to the beanbags and write notes in my journal with a mapacho hanging out the side of my mouth like a Peruvian Hunter Thompson.

It's time for me to let go of the shame from the failure of my first novel.

It's doesn't matter that I was rejected by every publisher I sent it to. It doesn't even matter if the book sucked. Because I learned from the process. I learned how to be vulnerable. I learned how to stop holding my cards so close. I learned how to open my chest, pull out my heart, hold it in front of me with both hands and say, 'Here, I made this, what do you think of it?' And while terrifying at first, once I got over the initial fear, it was liberating. Actually, it was exciting.

That's it, isn't it?

It's time for me to face the reality that I've been too afraid to name… If I've written a novel, and I've given it to someone, and they've read it, even if it's a piece of shit, as long as I haven't quit, then guess what: I'm a writer.

I am a writer. I am a fucking writer.

Say it out loud, Nick. Say it. *Say it!*

'I am a writer!'

Sam, swinging in his hammock, lifts his head from the book he's reading and says, 'Yeah, you are, man,' then keeps reading.

I am a writer.

Chapter Twenty-Three
The Storm

During my first stay at Way of the Spirit I generally chose a mat close to the door. This time around I seem to find myself on the far side of the Maloka. I run my hands over the skin of my belly, touching the new bone in my sternum. The chiric is out of my system and it seems to have done its job. I'm comfortable in my body. There's no cramping in my stomach. For possibly for the first time in my life, I feel a deep sense of satisfaction with my body, inside and out. I've been happy with the way I looked before but this is different. I feel clean. I feel cleansed. I feel… *healthy*.

I practise the breathing exercise Tony taught me during my first stay here. I breathe in deeply through my nose and into my belly. On my exhale, I visualise the air pushing out through my limbs, cleansing my body of stale energy. I breathe through my right arm for nine breaths. Then my left arm. My right leg, my left leg. Then my root chakra. Then my crown chakra. I repeat this breathing exercise twice more.

When it comes time for a second cup, as usual, I'm not feeling the medicine.

'A large one please,' I say. Isabella turns to Paulo.

'Oh-kay,' he says.

*

As the ceremony draws to a close, a sense of contentedness and warmth washes over me. This was a placid reintroduction to the medicine after the chiric. I remain on my mat while the others mingle and chat. It's not long before most begin to filter away out of the Maloka and back to their rooms. Isabella comes to ask how my night was.

'Gentle,' I say.

'I'm going into town with Ellie tomorrow night for dinner if you'd like to join us?'

'Sounds lovely.'

'Great. I'm going to bed now. Charlie will stay here in the Maloka for as long as you need.'

'I'll be fine,' I say, 'I'm heading to bed soon myself.'

A storm hits. Not a figurative storm, a literal storm. There's only a few of us left in the Maloka. Myself, Charlie and a few of the new guys. The bloke lying next to me was heaving into the bucket all night, but he's sleeping now. Rain flits through the flywire windows. The cool water is refreshing on my bare chest. The others are murmuring amongst themselves. I lie silent on my mat.

Thunder rolls in.

I close my eyes.

Holy shit. I am not *out of the medicine.*

Brilliant visions! Spiralling neon coral organisms, dazzling in form and colour, morph by kaleidoscopic means into unfolding pyramids of light. Folding, twirling seaweed structures. Expanding and contracting analogue shapes! I am the captain of a ship, navigating through shocking psychedelic waves, but soon the medicine becomes too intense, and I lose control, and I tumble helplessly through realms of space and time and it's all I can do to hold on.

In time, the waves die down. I return to the room and my mat, and I open my eyes.

Christ almighty!

That was a breakthrough DMT experience, no doubt about it. Instead of going back to baseline, though, I'm still buzzing and trembling.

How long was I gone?

I hear Charlie's voice somewhere in the distance. He and the others are heading off to bed. It must be late. 'Are you all good here, Nick?' he asks.

'All good, mate,' I mumble.

But as Charlie moves further away from me, it comes on fast, and it comes on heavy… The Fear.

I cannot be alone! I cannot be alone! I cannot be alone!

As Charlie reaches the door of the Maloka, I call out to him. 'Yes, mate?' he says.

'Do you mind hanging around a little longer?'

'Sure.'

I close my eyes.

And I'm on my ship again, gently sailing atop a black ocean. Thunder cracks.

A lightning bolt illuminates a mighty wall of dense fog in the sky, then pierces the ocean, and for one shocking moment, reveals a world of nightmares swirling below the surface where dark shadow creatures creep and crawl and scratch and claw.

My ship takes me to the wall of fog. There is no turning back now. On the other side, my ship is shattered to pieces, and I'm overwhelmed by unfathomable power. Nothing in my life could have prepared me for this. There is no joy nor fear nor pain, here in the darkness of the universe, just intense power. I scream in the darkness as I'm torn apart.

My consciousness breaks out of the ocean of darkness and blasts back into the room to join my hyperventilating body.

I breathe for my life. I breathe for something to hold on to. *Oh God. This is so intense!*

I turn to my side and laugh. Waves of joy. Waves of euphoria rushing up and down my body. Laughing. Breathing it in, laughing it out.

This is so fucking intense!

But then comes agony. The agony glues my eyes shut. I'm lying on my back, but the agony pulls me over, and I curl into myself. My vision is red and black. All is red, and all is black. Deep bleeding red. Twisting shadow black. Knives cut and impale. Claws tear away at my flesh. I feel all the pain and trauma of the people in ceremony. It's flooding into me and I'm taking it all on. A great ocean of blood envelopes me. I fall onto my back and clutch my legs up into my chest. The red is everywhere. I am choking. There is no air in this world. I've lost myself to panic. I can't breathe. I'm stuck. The red is everywhere.

My eyes open.

I can breathe.

The Maloka is dark. Charlie is still sitting on the mat next to me, staring into space. A bizarre sense of joy! It's a joy at being shown this pain and being allowed to experience it, and understanding what it means to feel, to really feel. But the joy soon vanishes, and I am with the pain again. This time it's *more* intense. This time it's more than the pain of the Maloka, it's the pain of the world, flooding into me. I'm an open vessel, and I'm taking in all of it. All the disease and famine and war and rape and trauma and abuse and suffering. It's all draining into me. The pain becomes unbearable. Tears silently slide down my cheeks. I am too shocked to cry. My stomach contracts with the pain. I have nowhere to go, nowhere else to be, but with the pain. My skin crawls with the pain. It tears my body apart. My mouth hangs open. The pain is incomprehensible. There is no face, no name, just pain. It's too much. I spend an eternity with the pain.

*

In time, the waves settle, and amongst the wreckage of my ship, I wash up to shore. Utterly broken.

'Thank you… Charlie,' I whisper.

And then I softly weep into my pillow.

Chapter Twenty-Four
Surrender

Ellie bursts through the flywire door of Pentagram to find me curled up in bed. I glance towards her but don't say anything. She sighs, then gently lifts herself onto the end of my bed and sits cross-legged. 'You missed breakfast,' she says.

I lift my head from the pillow to meet her gaze. I try to talk but can only manage to blubber and weep. She crawls up my bed and spoons me.

'Ellie, I'm broken.'

'This is what it means to heal. This is the work.'

Ellie holds me for a while. But we both know I need to be alone.

*

When I was in my early twenties – having entirely rejected the teachings of my Catholic priest – I figured that when I died, that would be the end of it. I held no illusions of heaven and hell. I would not live forever in paradise, nor would I burn for eternity in the fiery pits. I would simply become food for worms. With that in mind, I came on this journey with an agenda: to find a reason to live. If I didn't find one, then I would kill myself. That was the final card I could play, to silence the pain and confusion of living in this world.

But last night my final card was taken from me.

I'd considered before, theoretically, the concept of reincarnation. But I'd never felt the reality of it as vividly as I did last night. I realised the truth of my situation here, in the world as a human being. I realised that not even death can save me from existence in this horror show. Because when I die, this body will become food for worms, yes, but my soul will live on. My soul will pass through the shocking realms of the afterlife before it is plunged once again into the material world, and 'I' will be born again as a soft, innocent little blank slate. And I'll have to go through this bullshit all over again. Just as I've done hundreds, maybe thousands of times already. I'll be re-conditioned by my parents and whatever fucked-up, insane society I'm born into. I will forget everything I've learned in my past incarnations, and I'll stagger blindly through this brutal, maddening hellhole that is human existence. And so it will go. On and on and on and on and on. This is the karmic wheel. This is eternity. This goddamn eternity. This hell. We don't have to die to burn in hell because we are already living it. And there is no escape. Not even in death.

I'm sobbing on the floor of Pentagram now, struggling to breathe, choking through my tears.

This is a trap! It's hopeless. It's all hopeless!

Fuck, I'm gonna be sick.

I fumble around for a bucket.

Shit, I left it outside to dry.

I race around the corner into the bathroom and hurl into the toilet.

Hurling and crying.

Then leaning against the wall of the bathroom, exhausted and ruined, I glance up at the same laminated quote that was stuck on the wall in Casa del Graham. I drool over my neck, slide down onto my side and pass out on the bathroom floor.

*

Ellie comes again in the afternoon with a banana and a mandarin. I'm lying on my bed again, looking up into the ceiling. The horror of the karmic wheel has passed and left me numb and blank but at the very least, still in my body and still alive.

'You missed lunch as well,' she says, leaving the fruit on my writing desk.

'Too sad.'

'Are you going into ceremony tonight?'

'Tonight?' I just assumed I'd never drink the medicine again. I couldn't handle another night like that. If I go into another ceremony, I might never come back. 'I don't think so, Ellie.'

'It's only Sam with his name down,' she says. 'I'm going into town with Isabella tonight, and most people are on diet, so it will be a small ceremony. It could be perfect, Nick. It could be just what you need.'

There is something in her eyes. Her shining eyes.

She doesn't know me. How could she know what I need?

She's right, though, mate.

Please, no. I can't go there again.

'I have to, don't I?'

She smiles.

Of course, I do. What choice do I have?

*

The first person I encounter after stepping outside my house is Sam.

'How's it going, brother?' he asks.

'I think I'm gonna drink tonight.'

He smiles and shakes my hand. 'That's awesome, dude,' he says. 'I'll see you in the Maloka.'

'Do you know where Tony is?'

'He's with Christal. I'm sure it's cool if you swing past her room.'

I remember the photos of Christal's kids on her phone, the rash on her face, and the sadness behind her smile. When I get to her house, Tony's sitting by her bed trying to get her to take on electrolytes.

Margaret rises from her chair to meet me by the door. 'Christal had a bad reaction to a plant diet,' she says. 'She's been purging all day and her skin is inflamed.'

Tony turns to me. 'Are you heading into town tonight with the girls?'

'Actually, I'm thinking of drinking the medicine.'

'Well now, that's a curious turnaround.'

'I'd like to speak with you first, though, if that's okay?'

'Sure. I'll come to your house in about twenty minutes.'

*

Tony nestles into the hammock. I'm on a chair facing him. Tony wipes the sweat from his forehead with a handkerchief. I take a draw from my mapacho and tap the ash out into my bowl.

'It felt like the pain of the world was flooding into me.'

He nods.

'Sometimes,' I say, 'I feel guilty for feeling pain. It's like, I don't deserve to feel this way because I've lived a life of such privilege, compared to so many people. I see so many people living in poverty, and I feel helpless. And I feel guilty for my life. And even more guilty when I feel so depressed.'

Tony nods, then swings around on the hammock so that his feet are planted on the ground and he's looking straight at me. 'Fuck that,' he says. 'Your pain is your pain. You are entitled to feel whatever it is that you feel. There is incredible pain in the world, Nick, and you're allowed to feel it too.'

My eyes well.

'You're allowed to feel pain, man. It doesn't matter *who* you are.' He pauses and takes a drag from his mapacho.

'But my life is good, and still, I feel so fucking *sad!* I just want to curl into a ball and cry, and I don't know why? What's wrong with me?'

'There doesn't have to be a reason. You can just feel sad. There's nothing wrong with you. You're a human.'

I'm a human.

'And as a human, you're entitled to feel the full spectrum of human emotions.'

His words are a spell, an enchanted key that opens the locket guarding my heart. Sadness is a human emotion. Sadness is part of the human experience. Sadness lets me know that I'm alive. I experience sadness because I am a human. I am human.

'I think I know how you're feeling. You want to cure the world of suffering, don't you?'

I nod. 'The world is so unfair. I see all this trauma and I can't do anything about it.'

'I wanted to save the world too,' says Tony. 'You know what I figured out? It's not my job to save the world. And it's not your job to save the world either. All I can do is work on myself and help the people in my life as best I can. That's all anyone can do. One day you'll see that the easiest way to reduce the suffering in the world is cure your own suffering.'

In almost an off-hand comment I speak of my tendency to feel the medicine late in the ceremony.

'It probably has something to do with your metabolism,' he says. 'I'll mix up a batch of mouth orgasm for you, that might help.'

'Mouth orgasm? For this?'

'The cacao is an MAO inhibitor, plus the coconut oil should help metabolise the medicine. We used it a lot in the past for people who had this late-onset issue. The problem with the mouth orgasm is that it attracts ants into the Maloka.'

I take a deep breath.

'Nicholas. How do you feel?'

'Ready.'

'See you in there.'

*

Sam and I sit on opposite sides of the Maloka. Sam is near the door. I'm on the same mat as last night. This time, I am prepared.

Tony comes around to feed us each a spoon of the sweet black mouth-orgasm about half an hour after the first cup of ayahuasca. Sam begins to purge soon after. I'm seated cross-legged at the front of my mat, drinking water to help the mouth orgasm slide down into my gut. I rock back and forth with Sam's purge. I'm feeling it with him.

That's it, get it all out, I think to him.

Hey Nick, time to focus on your own process, mate.

That's right. It might get dark for me tonight. There might be something coming up that I have to deal with. My heart races with a kind of nervous, fearful excitement.

I could be sailing into the black ocean again.

Holy shit, man. This is real. This is heavy!

I pull my shirt off so I'm wearing just my boardshorts.

The shirtless jester with a sack tied to a stick.

I lie down on my back to work through Tony's breathing exercise.

I can take it. Whatever comes. I can take it.

The medicine hits me just as Paulo and Sandra begin a new set of icaros. Their songs radiate out to fill the room. I am crawling through mud under a thick black fog. And all around me, the ayahuasceros are building something with their soundwaves; it's some kind of mycelial network, a kind of vibrational structure, hanging in this pregnant darkness.

Whatever comes, I can manage.

Inhale.

Exhale.

And then I come to the Room of the Shadow Spirits.

This, I've not encountered before. Nothing like this, have I encountered before.

It's like looking through the double-sided mirrors of a police line-up, into the gallery behind, where there's half a dozen or so of these Shadow Spirits. I open my eyes, and the Room is still there, like a television screen superimposed over my visual field. The Shadow Spirits are humanoid figures, but their faces are veiled, and they have stretching, reaching limbs, but no hands or feet. They sway like dark seaweed, gently moving in a soft ocean current.

One Shadow Spirit speaks to me: 'Hello Nicholas,' it says. 'Nice to see you again. I want you to choose one of us, Nicholas. The one you think is the most playful. Choose one of us to come into you tonight.'

Fuck.

Me.

I am *deep* in the medicine.

You can do this.

Something feels off…

'No,' I say to the Shadow Spirit. 'Not tonight. Tonight, is for me.'

The Shadow Spirits turn and slip away into the darkness behind them. The curtains are drawn closed. The Room disappears into the fog.

A distant sound pulses.

It's 'On the Run' from *Dark Side of the Moon.*

Something is shifting. Something is growing. My body is being manipulated. Faint whispers in a strange tongue melt into the synth-waves.

I am not afraid.

Oh goodness!

Unfolding psychedelic landscapes! Moving organic coral organisms of neon light. Fractal bulbs and fronds of coral burst out from great pillars of colour and light. Multi-dimensional pyramid structures, enveloping and pulsing rectangular grids folded upon each other. An astonishing realm of beauty! There is no fear. There is just amazement. I have never known such endless beauty and complexity. I focus simply on breathing and try to maintain awareness. I'm in the Maloka and I'm in the vision. The realities have fused together. More moving, folding and unfolding of the visionary spaces. I fly through realm upon realm upon realm of these landscapes. Each emanation builds upon the previous. And they are endless.

This is Eternity without fear.
An Eternity of Beauty!

And then... I mustn't have noticed the *Language* begin, because...

Oh

My

Goddess!

... as though I slipped accidentally through some secret backdoor entrance...

...The same yellow and green overlay. The same bubbling and pulsing organic cavern of light and information. The same alien realm that I witnessed for the first time in Stan's backyard. The same strange and otherworldly language. *Thromping* and *Thandros* and *Thanatos* and *Thrall*. The same Realm that so terrified me with its alienness and its horrifying eternity during my second ceremony at Way of the Spirit... But there was no creeping up to the razor's edge this time. No peering over and wondering. No caution from the Mother. Without any awareness or warning, I've just slipped through to the other side. And now I'm in it!

The DMT Realm.
No...
No, I'm not *in* it.

I am it.

I *am* it!

I get it! I fucking get it!

It is within me! The Realm is within me!

The Realm *is* me!

'*Oh wow!*'

And… it is sexy! It is weird-sexy! The Realm is taboo, and it is freedom, and it is all-encompassing, and it is inescapable, and it is enticing. It's completely novel and yet overwhelmingly familiar. It's all bubbling and oozing and gyrating and folding and flowing and unfolding and glowing. It's a melting bubble pot of gooey sexual energy. It's a terrifying though utterly compelling, irresistible glimpse of the eternal divine. *Grolgy, grog, googly, goozy, goozy, growlgy!* It's multicoloured and sparkling, glimmering, astonishing! *Celsius*, it says! *Excelsior! Thanatos excelsior!*

…And the entities applaud my arrival.

Hooray! they cheer. *You made it!*

Oh, the Joy!

And I feel no fear, no terror.

Just Love.

Love!

I look at my body with open eyes and see thousands of little yellow minions, polyp-type entities moving about all over my skin. The minions are dancing, rearranging, fixing, melding, restructuring.

Astonishing!

*

With joyous breaths I depart the DMT Realm to delve deeper and deeper into unfolding psychedelic realms. I explore the layers of mind and consciousness. Deeper and deeper and deeper. I can search and probe endlessly if I so will. The fear and the terror are gone, though there is still the same relentless, urgent intensity to the experience. I have to work just to breathe and to hold on and to pay attention.

*

I've spent an eternity delving, and now I'm lying on my side, gathering my strength. The medicine is still overpowering my body, though the visions have softened out of focus. I'm becoming exhausted. I don't think I can take this much longer.

An entity speaks. 'Now, Nicholas, you have to piss yourself.'

I'm taken aback. *Nah*, I reply.

'*Yes…*' it says, slowly. 'You have to piss yourself.'

Other entities begin to taunt me. *Stinky pants, stinky pants!* they tease.

But I don't want to, I say. *Let me get up and go to the bathroom. I can make it to the bathroom. I know I can.*

'No.'

Then let me purge into my bucket, I reason. *Let me spew to release. That's fair.*

I don't want to piss myself. That's weird. I don't want to be weird. I don't want to lose my shit. I'm stable. I've got it together. I don't need to piss myself.

The energy turns darker, and I begin to worry.

Oh shit. The Fear.

'You have to piss yourself,' says the entity.

And the space grows darker again.

I resist. *No. I don't want to.*

'You have to face this, Nicholas.' *Stinky pants…* 'Or this will become a nightmare.'

Stinky pants…

The fog descends. Grey clouds surround me. A ship-hand readies a boat by the banks of the black ocean of darkness.

Goddammit. Fine. I'll piss myself.

A realisation.

I'm experiencing time in such a way that I have, indeed, already pissed myself. All that's left to do now, is allow it to happen. This will complete the loop. The decision has been made. This is my destiny. The path is there. All I have to do is let it happen. I turn from my side to lie on my back. I breathe. I am calm. I surrender to the process.

And, I piss…

The piss floods out and drenches my shorts and my mat and my blanket.

And the entities cheer!

You did it!

They're not making fun of me. They love me.

I am overcome with joy! This is a heavenly piss. This is the most beautiful piss of my life. The piss to replace all other pisses. I'm wetting the bed as a child. I am pissing my pants as a young boy walking home from school. I'm pissing on Timmy McVaney's shoes that day up at the bush. And I am pissing all over my mat.

The pure joy of letting go.

'It's okay, boy,' comes a voice. 'It's okay, boy.'

A beautiful pardoning. I'm okay. Everything is okay. I don't have to worry anymore. I don't have to be afraid or feel ashamed of anything. There's nothing wrong with me. There never has been, and there never will be. I am perfect, just the way I am. I am free. This life is only a trap if I see it that way. It's only a trap if I allow myself to be chained. I have the power to transform my existence. I have the power to transform what was once a trap into a beautiful opportunity for growth and love. Oh, the Joy! The Joy!

*

The moments following the heavenly piss are blissful, as I perceive my life in perfect clarity. I realise this piss, this last letting go, represents the closing of a loop, the completion of a cycle. It's a turning and closing of an arm of the Great Spiral that is both within and above and all around. The loop began that day I smoked DMT in Stan's backyard. And all the strange and mysterious steps along the way to this point were pieces of a great puzzle that have finally come together. The mysterious *Language*; the externalising of the DMT Realm as alien; the willingness to leave home; the disappointment in Urubamba; the cleansing of my body to be ready for the medicine; the glimpses of visions and the Fear; learning to love my body inside and out; the incredible pain of last night's ceremony; the total horror of reincarnation; and then the courage to face the medicine again tonight.

All the ceremonies, all the pain, all the fear, all the doubt, all the shit, has led me to this one moment of pure clarity. My realisation stretches out beyond that first hit of DMT and back into my childhood. The discomfort and confusion of religion in school, and the spark of curiosity in the health-class drug pamphlets. All those awkward teenage sexual fumblings – an ecstasy of shame and pleasure – with the girls I struggled to understand. Back further the make-believe worlds I constructed with my sister. And even further back to my own imaginary worlds, in the time before she existed, and it was just me and my parents. And now my clarity stretches far beyond my simple little life. And I sense deep, profound knowing. The places I went to tonight felt eerily familiar. I returned to *some thing* or some *place* or some *state* tonight. I was *remembering*. The information pours into me. I understand now that in my daily life, I've been guilty of forgetting a fundamental truth. I have spent my life lost in the belief that I am nothing more than a conscious meat sack called Nicholas. But my *body* is not all that I am. My *mind* is not all that I am. My *self* is not all that I am. I understand this now.

The medicine is one tool to help me *remember* what I really am. The priest at my school had it all wrong. Jesus was not the *Son* of God. He *was* God. And so am I. And so is everything else in the universe. That priest's cheap red wine was not the blood of Christ. This vine. This sacred vine is the blood of Christ. This is the holy sacrament. This is the way to commune with the creator. I understand Pierre Teilhard de Chardin. In all these world-shattering moments with the medicine, I am *not* a human being having a spiritual experience. No. In these moments, I *remember* that which was always true and which I always knew: I am an eternal soul, an expression of the divine, *God Itself,* having a temporary human experience. Profound clarity. Pure information. Perfect understanding.

What I started out referring to as the DMT Realm, when it feels like I'm surrounded by some kind of strange, pulsing sexual force, is nothing less than the universe making love to itself. Yes. The universe is making sweet, sweet, sweaty, breath-taking, uncompromising, orgasmic love to itself. And I am witness. And of course, this infinite and eternal sexual encounter is going on all around me, all the time. On a surface level, yes, all the animals and birds and insects and plants and all life is living, eating, fucking, birthing, dying, all around us, all the time. But I mean *everything*! I mean all the fucking molecules and particles and quarks and whatever-the-farks, are all dancing

270

the same sexy dance. I know that all matter is merely energy condensed to a slow vibration; the whole universe is vibrating constantly. It's just one big vibrator pleasuring *itself*! The universe is not random and empty and mechanical: it's bright and it's juicy and molten and gooey and gross and ugly and sexy and irresistible and beautiful and astonishing and it's happening all around me whether I acknowledge it or not. Aha… and then there is one more step, a final intuitive leap. Just as the DMT Realm is not *outside* me, the *universe* is not *outside* me either…

For I am an eternal soul, an expression of the divine, God Itself.

So, I do not *witness* the universe fucking itself.

The universe is not *around* me…

It *is* me.

I *am* the universe.

I *am* the universe…

I am the universe, fucking myself through eternity.

*

Paulo draws the ceremony to a close with his final icaro. Tony lights the candles. I sit up on my mat, back to the wall. I might purge, so I rest my bucket in my lap, with no fear nor apprehension, just a smile on my face. The smile of a man who has nothing but love in his heart, and the feeling of complete surrender to the power and beauty of the universe. I reach to the floor by my mat and take a mapacho. I bring the tobacco to my lips, light it, and smoke it luxuriously, ashing into my bucket.

Oh, glorious mapacho, how I love you.

Tony comes to me with fruit. 'How was your night?' he asks. I smile and laugh. 'The best night of my life.'

'Excellent,' he says, with a grin.

Tony returns to his mat. Paulo and Sandra lie peacefully. Sam is up and sitting as well.

'I'd come over and hug you, Sam, but I don't know how to work my legs yet. Also, I'm covered in piss.'

'Hey Nick,' says Sam, 'me too, buddy!'

'Fuck yeah!'

Before long, Paulo and Sandra excuse themselves from the Maloka.

'Thank you!' I say. 'I love you.'

They laugh. They must get that all the time.

Eventually, Sam and Tony leave for their rooms too, and I'm alone, still with the medicine, in the Maloka. I feel a brief fluttering of anxiety, and then I realise that I'm all good. That actually, I've never been better in my life.

I packed a change of clothes tonight. This was the first time I've done so, as though I knew I would need them. I shower in the bathroom then stand naked and smiling in the Maloka. My heart is exploding. I'm in love with the world. My life will never be the same.

Chapter Twenty-Five
The Dream Pods

In the morning I jump out of bed, sing in the shower and dance around my room, naked and free. I fell asleep last night with a smile on my face. I've never been so eager for the coming of day before in my life.

Today is the only day I've been the first person to breakfast. I drink my smoothie and it's the greatest smoothie I've ever tasted. I order eggs and they are the best eggs I've ever eaten. When Ellie walks through the flywire door I open my mouth but can't find the words I'm looking for. She looks at me and smiles. She knows.

Upstairs at the Big House we lie together on the floor.

'I love you, Ellie,' I say, turning to face her.

'I know,' she says. 'I love you too.'

Later in the morning, Sam joins us on the floor to make beautiful, sweaty spoons.

Just before lunch, Isabella plods slowly up the stairs. She doesn't have the same glow to her, and I wonder if maybe she had a few glasses of wine last night.

'Hey guys,' she says, 'I have some not so good news. You know Bill, the owner of Dawn on the Amazon?'

'The old guy with the skipper's cap?' I ask.

Isabella slowly nods.

'What's up?' asks Sam.

'He's dead.'

'What happened?' asks Ellie.

'It was in the storm on Friday night,' says Isabella. 'The wind was so strong that all of the windows of Dawn on the Amazon were blown out into the street. Bill was asleep in his room upstairs, and he was thrown out. He was rushed to the hospital on Saturday morning, but was already dead when he got there. Tony is in town now talking with the family.'

'Heavy,' is all I can manage to say.

Isabella nestles into a bean-bag next to Ellie, and we sit in silence for a while. I picture my papou in his hospital bed in the last moments of his life. I see the tubes in his mouth and nose, and the machine pumping his heart. He *looked* like my papou, but it wasn't him. The essence of my papou had left. I think that's the only time I ever saw my father cry. Months later, I was in a car with Dad, and we talked about that night in the hospital. 'If I ever become a vegetable,' he said. 'I'd like you to pull the plug for me. If you feel you can do it. I don't want to be kept alive by a machine.' I nodded. 'Of course,' I replied. 'The Doors,' he said. '"When the Music's Over". That'll be our code.'

'Well, I'm going to do some Tarot cards with Margaret now,' says Ellie. 'Isabella, would you like to come?'

'Yes, I think this is a good idea.'

The girls leave down the stairs, and Sam turns to me. 'Mapacho?'

'Fuck yes,' I say, accepting the stick of tobacco from my friend. I light it up and suck in the sweet smoke. 'There was this interesting moment last night,' I say. 'Right at the end, when I was on my own in the Maloka.'

'Were you still in the medicine?'

'The warm afterglow.'

Sam nods.

'I was feeling super high because it was the best night of my life. And I'm thinking to myself: *How the hell could I ever drink ayahuasca again?*'

Sam frowns. 'Oh! Because it felt so complete?'

'Exactly. Where could I possibly go now?'

'So?'

'Well, I realised, of course, that this experience was just the introduction to ayahuasca. To use the analogy of a video game, I've just completed *Level One*.'

'You just levelled up.'

'Although… now that I think about it. That might've just been the tutorial you play even before the game starts, just to figure out the controls.'

'Dude.'

*

I walk the path back to Pentagram. As I approach the turn off to my house, I spot a snake slithering into the bushes. I take another few steps down the path and a second snake slides out from underneath the wood planks at my doorstep. *Two snakes, huh…* My heart's racing but I feel a sense of calm, because *of course* there were two snakes underneath my house.

I sit at my writing desk, facing out into the jungle. The light that makes it through the treetops is tinged green and yellow. Birds hop along the branches and take flight. Insects hum and click and buzz in the constant orchestra of the forest. I light a mapacho, take a drag then rest it in my ash bowl and contemplate just what the fuck's been going on in my life these past few months.

*

The following day I join Charlie for my second coca ceremony. Charlie's room smells of burnt Palo Santo wood. We sit and chew coca for a while, forming a shared intention for the ceremony. Charlie instructs me on the process. When it's time, I lie down on the mattress at the side of the room and close my eyes. The drumming begins.

I approach the Great Tree and speak the intention:

I will travel to the world below to find my Dream Pods

And I spiral down like Alice, through the portal within the Great Tree. Tumbling. Tumbling. Tumbling. Around me spin snakes and green leaves and faces and wooden writing desks and exercise books and pens and plates of food and insects.

Eventually, I draw myself to the ground and step out of the Tree and into the underworld. My view is blocked by a great disc of light in the centre of my field of vision. I change perspective from first person to third and look down upon myself as though my consciousness were a bird in the sky.

I persevere through the underworld in search of my dream pods and come to a structure that resembles a back shed standing alone in an overgrown field. Inside are little vases, like

Egyptian canopic jars. Charlie told me before we started that some of these dream pods would be ripe and plump and colourful, and others would be dull and shrivelled and grey. Amongst the burgeoning shelves, four pods command my attention.

The first pod glows red. I take it in my hands and the world around me shifts to a school yard. I am a teacher. Sharp suit and a sharp haircut… Freshly shaven face. I stand in the centre of the playground as kids clamber around me, jostling for my attention. They laugh and cheer. I'm smiling but there are clouds in the sky.

The second pod glows orange. There is a woman with child. My chest jolts. The woman is strong and beautiful. She looks to me with deep love in her eyes. I feel profound warmth and pride.

A great dragon appears in the shed. It's an impressive figure, large and scaled with an enormous wingspan. I shoo it away, and it launches into the sky. Like a rocket, it spirals up towards the sun.

The third pod is emerald green. There is a property in the countryside. I'm in the garden. My hands are in the earth. Vegetables grow all around me. I walk a dirt path through the forest. I have a long beard, long hair. A young girl in a floral dress walks beside me and grips my index finger with her whole hand. The girl and I reach the top of a hill in the forest, and I lift her onto my shoulders. Together we look out at the enormous orb of light, radiating across the sky.

The fourth of the dream pods is grey. The big city. Cafes and apartments and traffic. Roommates. Trendy cocktail bars and nightlife. Coffee and cocktails and MDMA. I let it go.

I wander around the shed for a while, opening and closing my dream pods. Clarifying and exploring the visions, until I hear the beating of the drum. It's distant and faint, but unmistakable. I'm being called back to the world of the material. As the shed begins to fade away, I notice, just for an instant, from below a pile of discarded grey dream pods, a distinct stream of glowing violet light.

Charlie slows his drumming, and I return to my body in the room. I lift myself off the mattress and move back over to my seated position opposite Charlie, taking a fresh clump of coca leaves and driving them into the side of my mouth.

'I was listening to the spirits,' he says, 'while I was observing your body during the ceremony. I noticed three distinct Spirit Animals when I focused on your three energy centres in the head, heart and base.'

I sit captivated, coca juice sliding down my throat.

'The head,' he says, pointing to his brow. 'This centre is associated with the element of Air. As I was observing you, I perceived the image of a dragonfly.'

I gasp, and my eyes shoot open.

'Hold on.' He smiles. 'Don't say anything yet.'

I nod.

'The heart,' he says, holding his hand over his chest. 'This centre is associated with the element of Fire. For you, I saw The Dragon.'

I shake my head.

'And the base energy centre. The abdomen. Associated with the element of water. There I saw The Wolf.'

He smiles and nods and chews.

'I had a vision of an enormous dragon,' I say. 'It flew in right into the middle of my back shed!'

'I can't make this stuff up,' he says with a grin.

Magic.

'Now,' he says, 'tell me about the other night, the ayahuasca ceremony, when you asked me to stay with you. What were you afraid of?'

'I don't really know. I was afraid that ah… I guess that things would get dark for me? I don't really know exactly what I was afraid of.'

'The unknown?'

'I guess so. There's this fear I have, of going mad. That I'll go nuts and never come back. But when I went into ceremony the following night, ready to face anything, it was the most beautiful night of my life.'

'You went in with courage.'

We pause to chew.

'It's no coincidence that these powerful realisations have come for you at the end of your stay here,' says Charlie. 'You've had a lot to purge from your body, both physically and energetically. You had to get rid of those blockages. The spirit's been waiting until your body was ready to accept the medicine, before you could progress any deeper.'

'So, what now?' I ask. 'I've only got a few days left here before I go home. I don't want to dive right back in and open something I can't close.'

'That's wise. It seems your spiritual vessel has reached saturation point. You need to integrate what you've learned here into your life. Otherwise, the medicine can't do its work. After integration, your spiritual vessel will be ready to take on more.' He pauses to grasp a few green leaves between his thumb and forefinger and add them to the pile within his mouth. 'Each time you fill up, the vessel grows larger.'

'Do you think I should go to ceremony tonight?'

'If you have fear or doubt, then don't go. If you decide to go, then don't try to control it. Go in and surrender to the medicine. You can go in with this intention if you like: *This is for all of us.*'

We pause for a while to chew our leaves and to contemplate.

'I'm feeling apprehensive about going home.'

'It'll be a challenge, Nick, no sense denying it. Most people are afraid of living in their light. By that I mean, they're afraid to live according to the path of their true self. Most people are afraid of being free. In mainstream society, people are so used to living with pain and suffering that they're afraid of their own happiness, because it represents the unknown. When you live in your light, on your true path, there's no off switch and there's no going back. There's no lying to your true self. And that's the frightening part.'

'I've been trying to figure out what all my experiences mean,' I say. 'What I've been doing here. Ellie and Isabella believe we all have a 'higher self' that guides us along the path to our destiny. Most people ignore the calling of the higher self and reject the path. But maybe my journey with the medicine was laid out by my higher self, to help me learn something? But then I thought, what if the higher self is actually a projection from the current self into the highest imagining of what the self could become? The higher self is an *ideal*, but it pulls the current self towards it. Or, perhaps what I could interpret as signs left by my higher self, are actually synchronicities occurring in my environment, and I'm just able to notice them as I become more energetically open? Or, what if all this is an illustration of the power of my mind to construct a narrative around meaningless, random and chaotic events?'

Charlie smiles. 'Don't overthink it, mate. The truth is that this a mystery. It's not a problem for you to figure out with your mind. What matters is in here.' He taps his open palm on his chest. 'It's time for us all to evolve, Nick,' he says, after selecting a few more leaves of coca to slip into his mouth. 'To evolve with nature, as a part of nature. The plants will help us. They want to help.'

Floral consciousness!

I hug Charlie and thank him for all his help.

'This is real,' he says. '*Remember.*'

Chapter Twenty-Six
The Final Ayahuasca Ceremony

In the centre of the room, the large pot billows smoke, and around it sits softly quivering candles. Shadows creep along the floorboards. I'm on the far side of the Maloka, with Sam to my left and Margaret to my right. On the side closer to the door is Ellie. Isabella sits on the mat next to Ellie, though I think she's holding the space tonight rather than drinking the medicine. There are some new people as well, lying on mats closer to the bathroom. Next to the table of medicine and ornaments, Tony sits silently with Paulo. I sling off my shirt and lie down.

Inhale.

Exhale.

This is for all of us.

To the left of my mat are my mapachos, my lighter, my little wooden ash bowl and my torch. Against the wall is my backpack with my towel and spare clothes. To the right of my mat is my bucket.

Paulo rises from his mat and walks to the pot in the centre of the room. He's wearing those same long black pants and white singlet as he always does. He kills the smoke and carries away the pot. He returns to sit on his mat and starts to hum. His vibration is haunting and beautiful. I lie back onto my mat and close my eyes. The blood pulses in my gut.

This is for all of us.

*

'Nick.'

I rise from my mat and walk over to Paulo and Tony, and sit cross-legged before them. Candlelight flickers across their solemn faces. Tony pours the brew. I hold the cup to my lips and almost retch with the smell. I drink the medicine, then bring my hands together in front of my chest in a gesture of prayer.

'Thank you,' I say, and return to my mat.

It is done.

Margaret is the last to drink and then Tony blows out the candles.

Mother Ayahuasca, please guide me in my integration. Let me see what I need to see.

Lying on my mat, I make a prayer of gratitude. First to all the different parts of my body. One by one, I acknowledge and thank them. My stomach, intestines, heart, lungs, my liver, my kidneys. All my organs. My muscles, my feet, my hands, my bones. My brain. I thank all the people in my life. The people here at the centre. My friends and family back home. I thank the plants. Mapacho. Coca. Chiric. San Pedro. I even thank kambo, the gift from the frog. And of course, I thank the Mother: Ayahuasca.

Sometime after my first cup, Isabella delivers a spoon of mouth orgasm.

'Have a good night,' she says, and touches my shoulder. She's wearing a long dress that makes her look like a guardian angel.

And then on the mat next to me, Margaret is deep in the shit.

'Make it stop, Tony!' she cries. 'Please! Make it stop.'

Ugh, I groan. *This is heavy.*

'I want to die!' she cries.

Really heavy.

*

A strange and sinking black mass envelopes me. All around me are the brutal sounds of moaning and purging. My eyes water, and saliva pours from the sides of my lips onto my pillow. There's a frightening, sickening energy about. I curl up into a ball and rock. My mouth hangs open. I notice myself mumbling into my pillow. I can feel Margaret's pain. I'm breathing for her. The medicine takes over and I piss myself for her. I piss myself to make a commitment to confront whatever comes up.

Tony moves to Margaret.

'Can you sit on my legs please, Tony. I don't feel my legs.'

The room spins, and my body sinks deeper and deeper into the mat. Streams of salt liquid squeeze a path down my cheeks. Black clouds invade my mind. Head in the pillow. I resist the medicine. I don't want my experience to be intense. This is my final ceremony and all I want is a nice, gentle, psychedelic trip. But instead I feel like I'm taking on the pain of the others in the Maloka. They moan and purge into me. I'm vulnerable and open and I'm sucking in their sickness. I want to check out. The medicine is coming on too strong.

Inhale.

284

Exhale.

Surrender, release, allow.

There's no warning.

I purge.

A deep gushing spew into my bucket. I'm purging for the whole room.

This is for everyone.

Vile voluminous sickness. Be gone from my body.

Then, lying on my back. The visions come on hard.

No.

This is too much.

Fear.

Resistance.

Oh fuck. This is me tipping over the edge. Oh fuck! This is too much. I can't hold it back. I can't save myself from the medicine.

This is it.

Fear!

I've done it now. I've made a mistake. I shouldn't have come. This is the night I lose my mind. This is my destiny. This is the completion of the cycle. This is the moment I tip over the edge. This is what it was all leading to! I'm going insane. Holy fuck, it's finally happened. I'm losing my mind. I'm going insane. I'm going insane. I'm going insane.

It's crawling up my spine. Fear. Breathing faster and faster. Heart-rate rising.

This is it. Oh, The Horror! The Horror! I'll never get out of here. I'll never return from this. Oh, fuck! What have I done? This was one too many. Syd Drumstick. I've fucked it. I've lost it. I am insane.

This.

Is.

The.

End…!

Nick! Ground yourself, goddammit!

I pull myself up to a seated position, fear coursing through my body. Tension seizing each muscle. With shaking hands, I reach for a mapacho. My ash cup on my lap. I place the mapacho to my lips. I light and inhale.

Grounding, I say, as I blow the smoke onto my lap.

Inhale. Exhale. Grounding.

Inhale. Exhale. Grounding.

Inhale. Exhale. Grounding.

Until the mapacho is finished.

*

I sit up on my mat and bring my bucket to my lap. I sense Paulo is about to close the ceremony. I can feel him weaving through the energy and watching the spirits. I want him to close. *Sing your final song, Paulo!* I can feel the song on his lips. I want it to be finished. I want the warm safety of the candles. Please let this be the end. I want the lesson to be learned already. Please let it be over.

But Paulo doesn't close the ceremony. It's not time yet.

He knows.

I have more work to do. I place my bucket back down and sink into the mat. I remind myself to surrender to the process. I close my eyes and repeat my mantra from the start of the ceremony. And I dive back down into the shadow, for the last time, to search for a golden nugget I can bring back from the deep black ocean of darkness.

*

The memory comes to me the following day as I'm pottering around in my room. It arrives unannounced like a stranger to the door. I sit down on the floor of my room and gently weep. I remember it so clearly. So vividly. How could I have forgotten? I was ten years old and had taken a walk up the hill to the local bush alone. This wasn't out of the ordinary. I'd often go wandering up there for hours at a time. Sometimes I'd go with my mother. Sometimes with my sister. Sometimes my dog. But this time I was walking alone. And this time it was different. The air was sharper. The world clearer. I reached the top of the hill and gazed out at the suburbs and the city. I became overwhelmed. Breathless. Tears trickled down my cheeks. My heart thumped against my ribs. It was swelling up, like it was expanding in my chest. I spun around slowly, looking out into the bush and the city and the suburbs and it was beautiful and it was daunting and it was overwhelming and it was ordinary. I started laughing, and then I started crying. My heart opened right up, and I felt the sunshine pouring into it. I heard the music of the bush, the earth. The birds sung to me. The trees whispered to me. The sun shone for me. I was in complete unity with my environment.

At ten years old I had no frame of reference for such an experience. But I understand it now. This was my first mystical experience. This moment started me on the path. This was the trigger point.

But I also remember now, why I had forgotten this day. It's because when I walked down the path from the bush, through the trees, over the stones, out onto the road. And I walked down my street, quietly smiling and astonished. And I stepped back into my house, I saw my parents waiting for me on the couch. They asked me to sit down. I could see that both of them had been crying, although my father was doing a better job of hiding it. They were sitting on a couch together, but were not touching. There was a great divide between them, far greater than the physical distance. When I sat down opposite my parents, that was when they told me that they were going to be living in separate houses from now on. That we would be moving to a different neighbourhood. Away from the bush. That I was going to move to a different school. That everything was going to change. And the magic inside me faded away.

On the floor of Pentagram, I sit smiling with my back against the bed post. The tears have flowed away now, and I sit cross-legged, holding my younger self in my lap. I stroke the sun-bleached hair on his head. I kiss him on the forehead, and I hold him close to my chest. *You're safe now, boy.*

Chapter Twenty-Seven
Goodbye

Christal is beaming. She's sitting next to Ellie at the dining table in the Big House, her skin golden and radiant. The first time I saw her in the light of day she was withdrawn, pale and covered from head to toe in a peeling, flaky red rash. Now, she looks like she's just discovered the secret to the meaning of life.

'How's it going?' I say.

'I'm wonderful,' says Christal, and Ellie smiles.

'That's great,' I say. 'Your skin is clear.'

Christal begins to cry. 'I drank San Pedro,' she says. 'And I spent the whole day in love with myself. I felt so much love, for everything. And then, a few days later, my skin had cleared up.' She is sobbing uncontrollably now, but her mouth is stretched from one side of her face to the other with a gorgeous smile. 'I'm so happy.'

After breakfast, I wander upstairs to contemplate my existence on a beanbag. Ants scurry about on the floor. Mosquitos float in for the kill from their hiding places in dark corners. Wasps bang against the fly wire walls. I manage to write one haiku in my journal –

Fear! The wolf is loose,
From amongst my pile of clothes
Billy throws thong. Death.

– before Sam walks in and offers me a mapacho. I'm sweating into my bean bag by this stage. He swings gently on a hammock. We talk about ayahuasca for a while, then we light up fresh mapachos and compare the rules of cricket and baseball.

At lunch, Tony emerges from the kitchen with a jug of vegetable juice. He rests the jug on the dining table and greets the collection of guests.

Tony looks to me and smiles. 'I don't think you need another plant diet,' he says.

My interpretation: *Hey Nick, you're alright, mate.*

*

Late afternoon rays pierce through the sparse gaps in the jungle and dance across the wooden path before us. Ellie and Sam walk arm-in-arm just ahead of me. We're meeting Isabella in the Maloka for a farewell ceremony. A snake bursts out from under the wooden pathway. Ellie squeals. The snake lashes out, but Sam and Ellie escape. The snake turns to face me, blocking the path. I take a slow step forward, and the snake advances to match me. It's head slowly bobs up and down. This is the only way forward. I take off my thongs and hold them around my wrists. I take a few steps back. The snake holds its position. I run at the snake, then launch myself into the air, and when I hit the ground I run, and I don't bother looking back. Sam and Ellie laugh, and so do I, and we jog all the way to the Maloka.

When Isabella arrives, we drag four mats into the centre of the room and lay out our goodies. We're like kids at summer camp with a secret stash of candy. We have a box of nunu powder, two bags full of coca leaves, a small bowl of mouth orgasm, three sticks of Palo Santo, three sticks of sage, one bottle of Agua de Florida, one packet of Oreos and a brick of mapacho.

We sit cross-legged and take the time to lock eyes with each other in turn.

The universe transpired to guide our paths together for a moment in spacetime, but it will soon arrange for those paths to spiral away once again. I leave tomorrow. Sam will stay another month or so, and then he'll move to an Iboga centre in another country. Isabella is going home for two months. Ellie will continue her work here at Way of the Spirit.

Ellie is the first to speak. 'I would like to say how blessed I feel to have you beautiful people in my life,' she says. 'It fills me with hope for the future. And I would like to set the intention for this ceremony to honour each other, to remember the moments that we have shared on this journey and to offer blessings for the future.'

One by one we thank each other for being part of our journeys, and Isabella extends thanks to Pachamama, and then we reminisce. Isabella talks of the challenge of working at the centre, and Ellie listens intently. We talk of our past and what brought us to Way of the Spirit. And then we talk of the future.

'I thought I would work here forever,' says Isabella. 'This was my dream when I first arrived at Way of the Spirit. But I've realised recently that this is not my place. This is Tony's place. This is his creation. There's going to come a time when I need to create something for myself.'

I tell them about my fears, my hopes and dreams, my piss, my challenges. Ellie asks what I've learned during my time in the jungle. I pause for a moment to consider the question. 'Two things,' I say. 'If nothing else, I've learned two things: Life *is* worth living. And my suspicions as a child were right: The world *is* magical.'

'Here, here!' she cries. And the others cheer.

It's the early hours of the morning when we blow the candles out in the Maloka. We hug as one group on the polished floorboards, with the spider-web ceiling above. I tell these friends that I love them and that I hope in my heart we will all be in the same place at the same time, some time again in the future.

*

My story is coming to an end. Time was suspended while I spent a lifetime in the jungle. But now, as though time is compensating, it's rapidly accelerating. I close my eyes with weeks left for me at Way of the Spirit. I open my eyes and it's time for me to leave.

I came to the jungle hoping for an expansion of my consciousness outwards. I ended up with an expansion *inwards*. I have a greater connection to my body now. The medicine has taught me how to feel. I feel more pain, more sadness, more anger, more frustration, more joy, more love, more pleasure, more excitement.

Or perhaps the medicine didn't teach me *how* to feel, but rather, the medicine helped me to *remember* how to feel. Perhaps I was born into this world open, vulnerable and curious, and I *learned* how to shut down, repress and protect myself from the physical world, and from the emotional weaponry of the people around me. It's no-one's fault. This is just the way that culture functions. But the medicine has helped me to remove my armour. To understand that I don't need it anymore. She helped me to see that it was safe for me to be vulnerable in the world, as a man and as a human. This has been an initiation. Into what exactly, I'm not sure. But something has happened to me. And I know that I've been changed forever. I am not the same man that left on the plane from Perth some four months ago. I feel like I've woken up from a spell. And while I have no idea what I'm going to do with my life, I am not worried, because I know who I am. And I know what I am. And now anything is possible. You see, I may be The Fool. I may be the shirtless jester with a sack tied to a stick. But I am also a goddamn wizard. I am the writer of my own destiny. I am the hero of my own story.

*

After breakfast, I join Tony upstairs at his house. Surrounded by paintings and books, I thank him for his guidance. 'What you've built is extraordinary,' I say. 'My time here has changed my life.'

'You're a good man, Nick,' he says, and then we hug. I'm surprised at how much I needed to hear that.

Later in the morning, I sit with Charlie in his ceremony room. We chew coca and smoke mapacho.

'So, you're headed off today,' he says.

'Yep, that's right, back to society.'

He smiles. 'The work you do in here, with the plants in the jungle, this is the easy part. The hard part is integrating all this when you go back home.'

I nod but don't really believe him. 'The work here is pretty hard, Charlie.'

'I know it seems that way but trust me, the hard part hasn't started yet. It's when you go to the shopping centre, or when you have a job interview. Or when your mates want you to come down to the pub. That's when things become difficult. You want to forget what happened here,' he says, 'then start drinking pints of beer down at the pub again every weekend. What you learn over here is just revealing to you what you need to do to change your life back home. And here you've got people making your meals and cleaning up your house and looking after you. Just try living as open and free as you are now when you're back in the big city.'

'Thanks for all your help, Charlie, I can't really express what it means to me.'

He grins, the way he always does, as though there's a big secret he knows, and I don't. 'Best of luck to ya mate,' he says. 'And remember to stay present. Wherever you are, and whatever you're doing, because after all, there's no past and no future. Eternity is just one moment.'

About the Author

By day, Alejandro works as a teacher at a high school in a leafy green suburb of Perth. After hours he is a dedicated writer and psychonaut, who, on occasion, facilitates creative retreats with a small band of misfit artists in the West Australian wilderness.

Printed in Great Britain
by Amazon

83947412R00171